The Next Patient

Published by New Encounters Press, in the United States of America
New Encounters Press: admin@newencounterspress.com
Dr. J. Thomas Grant: admin@drjthomasgrant.com
www.drjthomasgrant.com

Copy edited by Michelle Hope

In this book the patients, doctors, nurses, health care providers, hospitals, agencies, entities and the like are fictional. They do not represent or identify actual people, institutions, businesses or other organizations. The author has chosen to write under the pen name Dr. J. Thomas Grant.

This book does not offer medical advice and is not a reference or guide for medical diagnosis or treatment.

ISBN - Paperback: 979-8-9861600-0-9
ISBN - eBook: 979-8-9861600-1-6

Library of Congress Control Number: 2022913937

First printing 2023

The Next Patient

The Incredible World of Emergency Medicine

Dr. J. Thomas Grant

To my wife and family,
I can never thank you enough for your support, encouragement, and love—and for your understanding of the nights, weekends, and holidays I missed being with you.

To my emergency medicine colleagues—ER docs, nurses, midlevels, techs, secretaries, volunteers, EMTs, paramedics, first responders, 911 dispatchers, and police officers—thank you for being there to help those in need 24/7/365. You are all amazing and greatly appreciated!

Contents

AUTHOR'S NOTE

The encounters described in this book are based on many years of experience as an emergency medicine physician in both academic and community hospital settings.

In these stories, the patients, doctors, nurses, health care providers, hospitals, agencies, and the like are fictional people and places. Their names do not represent or identify real people, institutions, or other entities.

However, the medical conditions, crises, emotions, tension, medical challenges, therapies, personalities, and teamwork are very real.

To provide privacy for those with whom I have worked and those for whom I have cared over the years, I've chosen to write under the pen name Dr. J. Thomas Grant.

For clinicians who may read this book, please remember that the time frame for these stories extends over many years. The available therapies have changed significantly during that time. Likewise, the approach to various diseases and injuries has been modified and improved upon as our understanding of certain conditions has evolved.

In describing these scenarios, it was not always appropriate or desirable to include detailed medical terminology or processes, or attempt to describe every facet or sequence of care. The book is not intended to be any sort of reference or guide for medical treatment. It does not offer medical advice. To assist those without a medical background, a glossary of frequently used medical terms in the stories has been included.

I hope you will find these encounters intriguing, and will share some of the excitement, tension, perplexity, humor, and astonishment I have experienced as an emergency medicine physician.

INTRODUCTION

The emergency room is an incredibly unique world existing on the front line of health care, confronting many extraordinary challenges. It is a dynamic and unpredictable environment in which doctors, nurses, and other medical professionals care for patients.

The breadth of diseases and trauma encountered is vast, encompassing all manner of illnesses, injuries, mental health conditions, poisonings, overdoses, epidemics, pandemics, and environmental or man-made disasters. It is beyond what the typical person could imagine, and, at times, it even exceeds that which emergency medicine physicians might envision.

In the midst of this extraordinary milieu, patients arrive unscheduled and in an unpredictable manner, occasionally stretching available resources beyond their capacity. This creates another pressing aspect of emergency care—the time available for evaluation, diagnosis, and treatment. The pressure of time becomes greatly magnified when critically ill patients suddenly and unexpectedly arrive.

Within this setting exists a continual stream of activities—patient assessments; incoming data and test results to be interpreted; procedures that must be performed quickly and efficiently; and interactions with patients, families, and colleagues.

Another facet of emergency medicine is the enormous diversity of patients with varied personalities, beliefs, values, cultures, religions, attitudes, expectations, hopes, and fears. Such heterogenicity can sometimes generate challenges with communication, understanding, and emotions.

A broad set of essential skills is necessary to adequately function in this type of environment. Substantial medical knowledge, decisiveness in the face of limited information, life-saving techniques, and critical performance under pressure are requisite abilities.

Emergency medicine physicians and nurses do not stand alone, however. They collaborate with a host of other personnel and resources, frequently operating as a broad-based team.

In the prehospital realm, ER physicians and nurses interact with paramedics, EMTs, first responders, fire department personnel, police officers, and poison control centers.

Likewise, emergency medicine physicians work with a variety of physician specialists, nurses, and other health care providers throughout the hospital and other hospital systems. They may also interface with unique services such as organ donation teams; epidemiologists; ministers and priests; public health officials; and city, county, state, and federal officials—even the Secret Service.

In my many years of emergency medicine, I have had the good fortune to care for tens of thousands of patients. Some of those encounters have impacted me greatly, leaving me with indescribable and unforgettable moments of joy, and other times inflicting emotional wounds that never fully heal. The patients I have met and the situations I have experienced in emergency medicine have changed me and molded me over the years in ways I could have never anticipated.

I have been encouraged by friends and colleagues to share some of my experiences—lessons I have learned, insights I've gained, situations I have encountered, and how I've been affected by what I've seen and done. I believe that by doing so, I may help others better understand and appreciate the circumstances they may encounter should they need to enter the unique world of emergency medicine at some point in their life.

The stories that follow are not arranged in strict chronological order, although they are grouped into two sections representing a couple of broad time frames. Most stories in "The Early Years" are in the context of my emergency medicine residency program, with a few during medical school. "The Later Years" include stories primarily from my time in clinical practice following my residency program—what some might refer to as "private practice."

Each story stands alone, allowing the reader to choose which encounter they wish to explore next. I have attempted to order the collection in a manner that helps to balance the many types of cases and emotions experienced in the ER.

It takes years of education, training, and experience for emergency medicine physicians to reach a level of competence that allows them to feel prepared to work in the emergency room, especially when they may be the only physician on a given shift in the ER.

A number of challenges must be overcome before reaching that threshold of preparedness—knowing the doors to the ER are always open, inviting the unknown, and continually awaiting *the next patient.*

The Early Years

Unfathomable

I stood back against the cold, tiled wall inside the major trauma room, opposite its open door on the other side. From that position, I could see the flurry of activity in the room without being in anyone's way. I was only a second-year medical student with a lot of new knowledge attained over the prior eighteen months, and yet I still didn't have enough understanding or clinical skills to contribute anything to the actual care of patients.

I had spent endless hours learning about human anatomy, biochemistry, molecular biology, cellular physiology, and a host of other "-ologies." I understood much about how the human body works at a microscopic and cellular level, but that knowledge was a long way from being able to provide patient care at the macroscopic level.

That night I had come to observe in the surgical area of the very large emergency department in the teaching hospital associated with my medical school. It was here that residents were delivering patient care after having completed their years of training in medical school. The surgery "pit," as it was so fondly called, was often the scene of instantaneous decisions and dramatic procedures that had to be done in order to save the lives of those critically injured in accidents or assaults.

In Trauma Room 4, on the stretcher before me lay a man who had been stabbed multiple times in the chest and abdomen. He was surrounded by a hierarchy of clinicians rapidly performing numerous diagnostic and life-sustaining procedures as his vital signs tenuously indicated marginal signs of life.

IV catheters were being placed into his arms and legs so that the blood he had lost externally and internally could be quickly replaced by IV fluids and units of blood. Tubes were being inserted to help the man breathe. A urinary catheter was placed to look for the presence of blood in his urine while also providing a gauge of ongoing kidney function. Blood was being drawn to run laboratory tests that would identify his hematologic and metabolic status in the hopes of getting him to surgery for more definitive treatment of his internal wounds. While the activities seemed chaotic and frantic, they were actually decisive and methodical, with each person performing their assigned tasks.

As every action was completed, the person responsible would announce its fulfillment in a voice loud enough for all team members to hear.

"Fourteen-gauge IV in right arm, Ringer's lactate flowing wide open." Almost simultaneously: "Foley catheter in place, urine grossly clear." Then: "Chest tube in the right chest, secured, attached to water seal." More confirmations rang out as additional tasks were completed.

X-ray and EKG technicians moved their machinery into place, timing their diagnostic tests among the priorities of patient assessment and treatment, edging clinicians out of their way in a flow of coordinated effort to save the man's life.

A senior surgery resident orchestrated the activities, standing back from the inner circle of clinicians surrounding the patient. He observed all that was happening, receiving and cataloging in his mind all the information flowing to him.

Occasionally, he would make a request or give an order. "Repeat vitals and one gram of Ancef IV, please."

As a medical student, I could not fully process the magnitude of activity occurring in such a compressed time frame. I understood the individual procedures and tests being performed, but I was unable to piece together the timing and sequence of the priorities in the man's resuscitation. It was as if I could recognize each of the various instruments in an orchestra but couldn't fully grasp how the timing, pitch, and duration of the individual musical notes would blend together to create the desired melody.

The senior resident conducting the patient's resuscitation, however, seemed to have a clear idea of the overall performance as he remained completely focused on each of the individual contributions and how they merged together within the right time frame to provide the necessary outcome.

Soon, in what seemed to me like the end of the first movement in a symphony rather than its final notes, the senior resident announced the patient's current clinical status and known diagnoses, signaling the immediate and necessary departure for the operating room upstairs.

With that pronouncement, several residents removed their gloves, tossed them into the wastebasket, and promptly headed out the door of the room. There were more patients to be seen, more emergent care to be provided. It was two o'clock in the morning on a Saturday, a peak time for injuries, assaults, and accidents.

A couple of the nurses and techs pulled together the equipment that needed to be transported with the patient and then started out the door toward the hallway leading to the elevators that went upstairs to the floor of operating rooms.

As the clinical staff exited the room with the patient, the cleaning staff swooped in and began restoring the room to its original condition—mopping up the blood on the floor that was mixed with antiseptic and other liquids while also removing all the trash from opened kits of instruments, empty bags of fluids, spent dressings, and the like. They knew the room would soon be needed again, so they worked busily to complete their tasks.

As the cleaning crew came in, I left to observe other areas of the surgical section of the emergency department, moving from one location to another. In addition to the hallway for major trauma, there was also a "minor hall" where patients with lacerations were being sewn up, broken bones were being splinted or casted, procedures were being performed, and patients were being evaluated.

The surgical section of the emergency department contained twenty-four rooms along with a line of chairs near the entrance where more stable patients sat as they waited for an available room. Beyond that area was the outer waiting room with forty to fifty more chairs for those with less serious complaints, reflecting a continuous triage process of all patients present in the ER.

After walking past most of the rooms in the minor hall, I returned to the major trauma hallway with its six large trauma resuscitation rooms. I headed toward the last room, farthest from the entrance to the surgical area of the ER.

I did not see anyone entering or exiting the room as I approached it, so I thought I might slip inside for a closer look at all the equipment the doctors and nurses used in the critical care they provided.

As I neared it, I could see the door was slightly ajar with only a six-inch gap to peek through. I didn't hear any sounds coming from inside the room, so I expected it to be empty. To my amazement, however, I saw a patient lying on a stretcher in the room, off to one side—not in the center, as was the case for all the other major resuscitations I had seen. As I gently pushed open the door, I was surprised to see no one with the patient—no doctors, nurses, techs, or family.

Lying on the stretcher was a small boy who appeared to be about six years old. There were no sounds coming from him—no whimpering, crying, or other noises. I glanced back down the major hallway, expecting to see someone walking toward the room. I wondered why no one was with him. For a brief moment, I questioned whether he was deceased, awaiting someone to take him to the morgue.

I cautiously entered the room, feeling apprehensive. As I came closer to the stretcher, I thought I saw the boy's chest rise and fall ever so slightly, and I believed I could hear the faint sound of air moving through the endotracheal tube that had been placed through his mouth into his trachea. I took one or two steps closer to see if my eyes and ears were deceiving me.

They were not! This young boy was alive!

Although he was otherwise motionless with his eyes closed, he clearly was breathing. I abruptly turned and dashed out of the room. I had read about situations in which patients appeared to be deceased and then somehow their life functions returned after they had been transported to the morgue. I thought that perhaps this was one of those cases. I had to let the doctors and nurses know the young boy was still alive!

As I briskly walked down the hallway searching for someone to tell, I noticed a nurse standing next to the medicine counter where drugs were obtained for administration to patients. She was the only person who was not moving rapidly from one place to another. As I approached, she turned and offered a warm smile.

"How are you?" she asked, perhaps noticing the anxiousness on my face, and then looked back to the medication bottle in her hand.

"Excuse me, but that child back in Room 6 is still alive!" I couldn't help but blurt out my findings, knowing that time was critical in a situation like this—just as it had been with all the other patients in the major resuscitation rooms that night.

The warmth on her face disappeared quickly. It was replaced with a blank look as she stopped drawing up the medicine from the bottle into the syringe she held in her hand.

"Are you one of the medical students?" she asked as she refocused on the medicine in her hand, expression returning to her face.

"Yes, ma'am, I am. Second year." Her question caught me off guard. I expected her to immediately drop the bottle and take off running down the hallway, grabbing a couple of residents along the way. I wasn't sure she had heard me correctly.

"I saw the child breathing! He's still alive!" Thinking I hadn't adequately conveyed the important message initially, I attempted to speak clearly and distinctly, with greater urgency in my voice.

She set down the bottle and the syringe and looked at me again. I guesstimated she was about twenty-five years old and could not help but notice her big brown eyes. She had a look of compassion about her rather than surprise or urgency.

"I know," she said softly. "He's in Room 6 so he can pass on." She looked directly into my eyes, perhaps anticipating my response.

"What?" It was all I could say. I wasn't sure I had heard her correctly, but I was afraid that I had.

The disbelief on my face was easy for her to read. She reached out to me and gently took me by the arm, turning us back toward the hallway I had just come down. She began to speak as she slowly walked back toward Room 6.

"He won't live." She looked down as she spoke quietly. "He has a broken neck, a fractured skull, a terrible brain injury, and a lot of internal bleeding." She stopped when we reached the doorway.

Not accepting the hopeless finality of her statement, I asked, "But how do you know he won't make it unless you try to save him? Why is no one trying to save this child?" I held up my arms out to my sides in a gesture of disbelief.

"We did. We tried all that we could at the time, but as his injuries became evident, it was clear he could not survive." Her soft brown eyes conveyed her empathy for the child and for me in my angst. But it was hard to accept her words. I knew the reputed skill and abilities of the clinicians who worked in the surgical section of the emergency department—they were exceptional, second to none. I had witnessed them myself.

And here was I, a second-year medical student who had yet to take care of a patient, my only résumé a knowledge of molecular interactions, biochemical processes, and anatomic dissections on nonliving tissue. Yet I struggled to grasp the concept of giving up the battle to save a patient who still had signs of life—especially a child.

The kind nurse managed a slight smile in an effort to ease my mental anguish and said, "I'm sorry. There's nothing more that can be done." No doubt she had trodden this path before, familiar with addressing those of us who had never encountered a person in the process of dying, someone for whom life was slowly and certainly leaving their body. Witnessing that final stage of transition in which the last remnant of life slips away was not something I had anticipated.

"They are still trying to contact his relatives," she said as she turned her head to see an injured patient on a stretcher entering Trauma Room 1. "I'm very sorry, but I need to get back to my patients." With another reassuring smile, she turned and headed back down the hallway, resuming her efforts to treat those who still had a chance for life.

I stood outside the door to the room for a short while, trying to fully process her words. My mind did not want to accept the conclusion reached by others who, unlike me, had real clinical knowledge and experience.

How could you know with certainty that someone was going to die, that there was nothing else that could be done? Again, I thought about those people who lived after being declared dead and sent to the morgue. Certainly, it was rare, but it did happen.

But as I reflected more deeply on her words, I knew she had only given me a partial list of the young boy's injuries. And even though I hadn't yet entered the clinical world of caring for patients, I began to wrestle with the probability that the child's multiple injuries would almost certainly result in death in the short term, and definitely in the longer term.

I walked back into the room. It was very quiet except for the faint sound of the boy's breathing. I stood beside the stretcher on which he lay. I now could see the substantial bruising on the side of his face and head from the skull fracture she had noted. Other than that, there was no grossly visible evidence of the multiple injuries to the inside of his body, any one of which might ultimately cause his death.

Nonetheless the boy was still alive—his life had not yet ended. Accepting death when there was still life seemed incongruent with my inner being and my own life experiences. It was a dilemma I had never been exposed to or struggled with.

Those moments at his bedside seeped deep into my soul. Life is so precious, and so delicate.

A storm of emotion enveloped me in the weeks that followed as I contended with the issues I had faced that night in the ER. I thought about how such a brief moment can end a life filled with activities, memories, dreams, friends, families, and loved ones. I thought about the pain his family must have felt at his loss. I thought about how time cannot be turned backward to prevent such tragedies and how time forces us to move forward carrying burdens that seem unbearable. And in the midst of this emotional pain and suffering, I thought about faith, and how faith provides hope, and how hope can make the unbearable, painful—yet barely tolerable.

That night, I could not have anticipated how often emergency medicine would require me to confront that impending transition from life to death, and battle against it—sometimes successful and other times not. Each failure seemed to leave a wound that slowly became a scar, the deepest of which would ultimately be associated with my own family.

Seconds Count

They had told us what to do if it happened. I just didn't expect it to happen to me.

It was the beginning of our third year in medical school. Our clinical rotations would fill the next two years of our education in a much more intense fashion than what we had experienced in the first two years.

For the next several weeks, we would participate in a number of orientation sessions, familiarizing us with different areas of the hospital and how they functioned. Today, our small group of four students was rotating through the operating rooms (ORs).

Although our medical school class was large, the four of us knew each other. Liz, Ally, and Robert rounded out our group. Robert was a tall, slender, quiet, soft-spoken young man who already knew he wanted to be an ophthalmologist.

Ally was also quiet and studious. Unlike Robert, she was barely five feet in height. She wasn't sure which area of medicine she would ultimately pursue.

I knew Liz best. She had become a good friend. Occasionally, we would study together, quizzing one another about various details or minutia on whatever topic we were reviewing. There was a little competition to catch the other in something they didn't know.

Liz had a quick wit and a good sense of humor. She was slender and nonathletic, and enjoyed giving me a hard time for being a "jock," since I was playing lacrosse on a team with some of our male classmates. She frequently suggested I visit the outpatient psychiatry or neurology department—in her words, there must certainly be some type of brain dysfunction that would cause one to play such a foolish and injury-prone sport.

Prior to us entering the OR, we had been informed of what we would encounter—the roles of the anesthesiologist, surgeons, nurses, floaters, and all the other people involved in various types of operations. We would see the preparation and implementation of the "sterile field" in which operations took place and how the different clinicians maintained that sterile field.

The first OR we entered was one in which the patient was undergoing a skin graft for a burn. In our blue scrubs and surgical masks, the four of us were ushered into the room after the anesthesia had begun. We were to stand next to the anesthesiologist, which allowed us a view of the operating field from the head of the operating table.

The environment of this teaching hospital was wonderful. Most everyone wanted to help medical students gain a solid foundation for patient care in their medical careers. Both the medical school and the teaching hospital were nationally known for providing excellent medical education and exceptional medical care. It seemed everyone wanted to contribute to upholding that reputation.

The first thing I noticed as I came into the OR was the odor, about which they had informed us. It was a difficult scent to adequately describe. There was a metallic or chemical component to the aroma with an absence of other more recognizable elements, making it somewhat pungent. Part of the odor may have come from the hint of the anesthetic gases along with the "scrubbers" that were designed to eliminate, or at least minimize, the presence of gases in the operating room. It wouldn't be good if anyone but the patient were impacted by their effect.

There was also the scent of the antiseptics used to prep or sterilize the skin in the area of the operation, along with the smell of the sterile drapes and gowns used as a barrier between the bodies of those in the room and the operating field. They, too, had that chemical-metallic odor.

The sterile drapes were positioned in a way that allowed the anesthesiologist, and us, to see the head of the patient as well as the operating field.

On the unsterile side of the drapes, closest to the anesthesiologist, we were able to see the patient's face, her eyes closed and her mind completely unaware of all that happened around her and to her.

On the sterile side of the drapes, where the surgeons stood, the germ-free blue-green drapes closely covered the girl's body, exposing only her left arm and left leg. These were the sites for the operation. The anesthesiologist explained that her left arm had a severe thermal burn from a hot metal object, to which a skin graft from her left thigh would be applied.

Two surgeons wearing masks, sterile gowns, and sterile gloves would work on the girl's arm preparing it for receipt of the skin graft, and two other similarly attired surgeons would work on the patient's thigh to "harvest" the skin that would be used for the graft. The surgical steps in this process were not something we had been exposed to before.

The team harvesting the graft from the leg had a dermatome, a piece of equipment used for obtaining the skin graft. It was rectangular in shape, about four by six inches in size, with a black cylindrical handle on one of the long sides of the rectangle. I had not seen the device before, so I focused closely on it during the operation, watching the surgeon make some adjustments to it before turning it on.

Once on, it sounded like the electric hair clippers a barber might use to cut one's hair—sort of a low humming noise. One of the surgeons then positioned it against the skin of the young girl's left thigh. I watched as he began to move it down her thigh from top to bottom. I was fascinated to see how this machine would generate a skin graft.

As the surgeon applied some pressure to the device, I could see a thin layer of skin coming out on top of the device at the end closest to us, near the upper part of the patient's thigh. It looked wrinkled and sort of bunched up as it emerged—completely unlike the smooth, supple, healthy-looking skin of the girl's leg. That seemed a little odd to me, although I had never seen a skin graft before.

Then something caught my eye. I noticed streams of blood briskly flowing from the area underneath the dermatome. At first, I thought something must have gone horribly wrong with the instrument.

The dermatome had removed an upper layer of skin, revealing the middle portion of the skin, or dermis. It looked like a very deep abrasion with lots of red dots oozing blood against the background of the lighter-colored tissue.

In this case, there seemed to be a lot of blood—certainly more blood than I had anticipated.

Suddenly, a wave of nausea came over me. My mind reflected upon the blood coming from a surgically imposed wound that only seconds before had been perfectly normal skin. That wound now appeared excessively raw and bloody. I couldn't help but think of how terribly painful that procedure would be to a person who was awake.

I shifted my gaze to the other side of the drapes, looking at the peaceful sleeping face of the girl. My mind intrusively focused on how distressing it would be for this young person when she awakened. I thought about how awful it was for a child to have to go through such an uncomfortable procedure.

The smell of the room abruptly became much more prominent. The odor intensified my nausea. I could feel myself getting light-headed. Immediately, an alarm went off in my mind.

They had warned us about this. If one passed out in the operating room, the person could fall forward toward the operative field, contaminating the sterile environment. Alternatively, one could fall to the floor or onto the patient, which could injure one or both people.

They also had told us what to do.

Without explanation, I abruptly turned and exited the surgical suite, entering the hallway outside the OR. My knees were wobbly. I hurriedly leaned back against a wall and immediately slid down to a sitting position on the floor and put my head lower than my knees—not quite touching the floor but close to it.

Minutes went by as I remained in this position. Slowly, I started to improve. The light-headedness began to fade, and a little while later, the nausea abated. Still, I sat on the floor, watching people walk by and give me a look and a smile. No one stopped to see if I was OK. I'm sure they could tell I was a medical student, and they had probably seen others like me before.

Our clinical instructors had encouraged us to take our time before getting up again, and to do so slowly. Sometimes people stand up too soon or too rapidly. Doing so allows the blood to pool in the dilated blood vessels in one's legs, depriving the heart of an adequate amount of blood to send to the brain, causing the person to pass out and crash to the floor.

Although it seemed like an hour, only about fifteen minutes had passed before the remaining three in our group exited the OR, all talking about what they had seen and learned, amazed at how the skin graft was done. Robert and Ally headed down the hallway toward the next area we were to visit, acting as if I weren't there so as to not further embarrass me.

Liz, however, hesitated for a moment. I looked up at her, anticipating some sympathetic words for my ordeal. She smiled. The long, curly, thick black hair surrounding her face was silhouetted against the overhead lights behind her.

"Jock," she said as she stared at me, lingering for a moment just to be sure I heard it. "And a big, tough lacrosse player at that." She paused long enough for me to see her face transition into a broad smile, her eyes dancing.

"R…i…g…h…t," was the last word I heard as she turned and walked past me down the hallway, leaving me on the floor to slowly rise on my own. My mind could see her continued smile even though she was looking the other way.

While I wanted to hop up, quickly catch up to her and offer some clever comeback, I knew I shouldn't—and probably couldn't. Nothing would be worse than to make that effort only to fall flat on my face and truly add injury to insult. I stayed put, accepting the fact that she had achieved the clear advantage in this initial foray into the surgical arena.

That situation was the first of several experiences that helped me eventually understand why it was important—at times even essential—to be able to compartmentalize specific feelings one might have when treating patients. While empathy is a very desirable quality for a physician, it has to be appropriately managed. Early in my next year, that lesson would be much more greatly impressed upon me.

My fourth and final year as a medical student began with a one-month elective rotation in the surgical section of the emergency room. Similar to the residents, we would work five twelve-hour shifts each week, at times shadowing surgery residents. Depending upon which resident one worked with, it could be a wonderful learning experience or a minimally beneficial activity.

Some of the residents, especially the more experienced ones, enjoyed taking students under their wing. One night, I was lucky enough to be on shift with a third-year surgical resident, Mike Simmons. It wasn't often that third-year residents would be in the surgical ER. Most were first- and second-year residents.

Mike was an excellent teacher. He was very knowledgeable and remarkably skilled. On a rare, slow evening, he asked why I wanted to go into emergency medicine. At the time, the specialty of emergency medicine was just coming into existence and many faculty physicians at our teaching hospital discouraged me from pursuing that field of medicine. They strongly suggested I follow a more traditional specialty such as neurology, orthopedic surgery, pediatrics, or some other rotation I had enjoyed and in which I had performed well.

I conveyed to Mike my love for the investigative type of work the emergency room required, along with the need for decisiveness and a breadth of procedural skills. I told him how much I enjoyed every specialty of medicine—I found them all challenging and very interesting. Mike seemed to understand my perspective. I even thought he might share some of my views.

Slyly, I later talked with one of the more tenured nurses in the surgical area of the ER, telling her how much I enjoyed working with Mike and that I wondered if there was a schedule that showed when he might be on again. Of course, I knew there was a schedule, but that it was also kept secret for some reason I couldn't grasp. Eventually, she told me where they kept it, and one evening, I slipped into the room to check it out. Once I knew which shifts Mike was on, I traded as many of my shifts as I could to synchronize our schedules as much as possible.

On one of the night shifts, I was shadowing Mike when a very serious trauma case came in during the early-morning hours. As they wheeled the patient into the major trauma room, a covey of clinicians swiftly surrounded the patient and began performing the necessary procedures. The patient was critically injured from a high-speed vehicular accident that had killed two other people in the same car.

The patient was semiconscious and moaning in pain. I didn't know all the injuries he might have, but I could easily see multiple broken bones. I thought Mike would be the team lead, but there was a second-year resident who was given that responsibility. I assumed Mike was probably watching him while he also was instructing me.

Mike knew that among the many procedures this patient needed to have rapidly done on him, a chest tube had to be quickly inserted into the right side of the patient's chest. In the midst of the seemingly chaotic activity surrounding the patient, Mike stepped to the patient's right side and announced, "Chest tube going in on the right." At the time, I didn't know how he had made that decision.

Mike briskly nudged me into a position between the patient's right chest and himself. The nurse hurriedly pulled up a chest tube tray containing all the necessary sterile instruments and equipment. While I intellectually knew what needed to be done from our studies, there was a big gap between knowing and doing. There was a saying at the teaching hospital, "See one. Do one. Teach one." I had already seen more than one.

After I quickly put on sterile gloves, Mike told me to grab a handful of sterile gauze pads upon which he squeezed antiseptic solution from a bottle and instructed me to prep the chest wall. The activity we were a part of was moving at what seemed to be a frantic but deliberate pace with things happening all around us at high speed. After rapidly prepping the chest wall, I turned back toward the tray. Mike already had his gloves on as well.

Mike handed me a syringe of lidocaine, a local anesthetic to numb the tissue before the procedure. He asked me for my landmarks and for the specific location where the tube would be placed. I promptly responded with the correct answers. He nodded and said to go ahead.

I injected the skin along the top margin of a rib on the side of the chest wall, in an area known as the fifth intercostal space. Mike was pushing me to go faster, which I did. I knew if lidocaine was injected too hurriedly, it would burn. In this situation, time was a higher priority.

When I returned the syringe to Mike, he handed me the scalpel. "Go," was his admonition. I could tell he read my mind when I hesitated, knowing the anesthetic had not had enough time to fully numb the tissue. "Go! Now!" was his firm response with an urgent look on his face.

I immediately turned back to the patient and made a rapid, linear one-and-a-half-inch incision along the upper margin of the sixth rib, cutting through the intact skin and revealing the subcutaneous fat layer beneath. I could feel Mike's eyes following my every move.

When I turned back, we exchanged a large, curved Kelly clamp for the scalpel. "Spread the tissue," Mike emphatically said. I knew what that meant. I was to push the Kelly clamp, which looked like a long, skinny pair of blunted scissors, into the muscle that ran between the ribs and then spread apart the ends of the clamp, causing it to tear apart the tissue in that specific area. I thought about how painful that would be for the patient. Normally, one would make a second injection of lidocaine into the muscle to lessen the pain.

My momentary hesitancy resulted in another firm and chastising statement as Mike once again read my thoughts.

"Do it now or I will!"

I knew I had only a second or two before he would be standing where I was. I immediately turned, inserted the Kelly clamp, and spread it wide enough for a large bore hollow tube, about the size of one's index finger, to follow. The man, still semiconscious, let out a cry from the pain he felt as the muscle ripped apart.

Before I could turn around, Mike was handing me the clear plastic chest tube that I inserted through the hole I had created in the man's chest wall, threading it toward the back and upper part of the patient's lung. Without turning, I handed the Kelly clamp over my shoulder, knowing Mike would be handing me the instrument necessary to sew the tube into place, after which we made the connections to the equipment that would suck out any extra air and blood from the chest cavity, allowing the lung to fully expand. That expansion would now help improve the oxygenation of our patient's blood, which would be critical to his survival.

Having completed my task, I loudly said, "Chest tube in right side, secured." I then quickly listened for air movement with my stethoscope and said, "Breath sounds present and clear on the right." When I looked up, I noticed the resident on the opposite side of the patient finishing up the same chest tube procedure on his side of the patient.

After several more minutes, the trauma resuscitation was complete and the patient was whisked away to the operating room upstairs. Mike pulled me into one of the small consult rooms off to the side of the major trauma hallway.

"You did good," he said, pausing for just a moment, "but you cannot hesitate. You cannot let your concern for what the patient might feel override what the patient needs to save their life." He let that sink in for a moment as he intently looked me in the eyes.

"This patient had bilateral pneumothoraces. He wasn't getting much oxygen until we expanded his lungs with the chest tubes. Without them, pressure could have built up in his chest cavity. That would have kept his heart from adequately filling and he would have died."

He continued to look me in the eyes. His voice was urgent in tone but not demeaning or accusatory. Clearly, he felt this was an important concept I needed to learn—especially if I were to be a physician specializing in emergency medicine.

"Seconds actually count—it's not just a saying. A patient may have a normal heartbeat in one second, and the very next second, it can be gone. And getting it back is not always possible." The words sank deeply into my brain, and I never forgot them.

"Waiting thirty seconds to let the local anesthesia work could have killed your patient." My brain recognized what he had said—"*your*" patient. He continued, "You never want that to happen."

He shifted his body position, and I knew his valuable lesson was over. I expressed to him my sincere appreciation for walking me through the procedure and instructing me how to do it the right way. I thanked him for taking the time to teach me this very important principle, one that I never forgot and steadfastly incorporated into the care of my patients.

He finally smiled and said, "You're gonna do well. Stay with it." We headed out of the consult room and returned to waiting patients.

While the concept was easy for me to understand, it still took time and additional experience before I felt capable of "flipping the switch" whenever necessary. For many people, it can be very difficult to set aside, even temporarily, the empathy one strongly feels when caring for sick or injured people.

In specific situations, one must be able to logically assess the scenario and do what is called for under the circumstances, readily putting aside emotions that might delay or interfere with the performance of life-saving procedures. Doing what *must* be done, *when* it must be done, can indeed mean the difference between life and death.

That crucial lesson helped shape me into the physician I needed to be for the many difficult and challenging situations yet to come as an emergency medicine physician. Learning that essential principle greatly benefited me—and my future patients.

Come On, Doc!

Financing medical school was a challenge. I had paid my way through college by working on weekends, holidays, semester breaks, and summers. I had hoped to do the same through medical school, but I soon recognized that wasn't a realistic option. There wasn't nearly as much time off, so covering expenses through work was more difficult. Thankfully, those of us who needed financial assistance were able to get loans with relatively low interest rates.

Still, I looked for the opportunity to work whenever I could.

In my last year of medical school, I had a chance to take a job at the city jail. It was located in the downtown section of a large metropolitan area, which was not too far from the medical school.

The job consisted of providing "first aid" to prisoners at the jail after business hours. If I encountered something potentially serious that I felt uncomfortable handling, I had two options—I could call the large county hospital emergency department and describe the situation, asking for recommendations, or I could simply instruct the officers at the jail to transport the prisoner to the emergency room.

Even with that degree of backup, I was still hesitant to act on the opportunity. I was only a medical student, and concerned about situations that might arise for which I would be unprepared. There would be no testing equipment, and my treatment options were mostly limited to antiseptic, Band-Aids, Tylenol, and some antacid tablets. I felt like I would be on the front line of medicine battling disease with a toy gun.

Despite my reservations and some anxiety about filling the role, I applied and was selected as one of the individuals to staff the after-hours shifts, which lasted from six in the evening until six in the morning. With a group of us to provide coverage, individuals could sign up for shifts that wouldn't be followed by hospital duties the next day.

When the time came for my first shift, I headed to the jail after finishing my hospital rounds and responsibilities. As instructed, I parked in the underground basement and took the elevator up to the floor with security. From there, I passed through several metal doors, eventually entering the jail itself.

I walked into an open area called the "intake" where incoming prisoners were processed. On one side of the very large room was an officer sitting at a counter behind a wide glass window, which I presumed to be bulletproof.

As I entered, an officer in the area recognized my scrubs and came forward to greet me. He introduced himself as Sam, and began my brief orientation. I followed Sam toward a narrow hallway that led off from the opposite side of the intake area. When we got to the end of the hall, Sam unlocked a metal door on the left.

"Well, here it is," he said as he stood in the open doorway, waving his arm as if he were on a game show directing people's attention to the prize now appearing from behind the curtain.

I glanced around the room. The walls consisted of concrete blocks, painted a drab gray color, like much of the jail. They were bare, with nothing to break up the sea of gray. The room was about ten feet by twelve feet with a dim fluorescent light overhead. Inside the room, directly across from the open door, was a small bunk, just big enough to sit on or sleep on.

To the right of the open door was a small metal desk on which sat the "first-aid equipment"—a minimal amount of over-the-counter treatments. There was also a telephone on the desk. A plastic chair with metal feet, like one might find in a school cafeteria, was pushed forward under the desk.

This was it. The first-aid station in all its glory!

"It's a beauty," I said with a smile as I walked in and looked around, setting my armful of books and my black "doctor's bag" on the metal desk. The bag contained a number of medical instruments I had used during my rotations in medical school. It also contained a few "bedside tests" I could run if needed. "Nice and cozy," I added.

Sam explained how the process would work. Typically a couple of officers would bring a prisoner to me whenever possible. That would pose the least risk to me. At times, the prisoner would be freshly processed into the jail, and other times, it would be a prisoner who had become ill after being in his cell for some period of time.

My room was referred to as the "medical station," a glorified description of where "first aid" would be offered. Eventually, I would learn that it was more about triage than treatment. After all, there wasn't much first aid to offer.

It was clear to me that this room would be my abode for the next twelve hours.

"Any questions?" Sam asked.

"I don't think so," I said, imagining I might have some as the evening progressed.

"The number for our front desk is on the phone. So, if you do need something, just give us a call." With that, he managed a smile and headed out of the room. The heavy metal door closed on its own behind him.

For a moment, it seemed as though I had been locked in a cell also. The room was cool, dark, and dreary. Of course, I could open my door if necessary, but they preferred I stay put. My mind jumped to the positive—I would be earning money! It wasn't much above minimum wage, but it was money! And I hoped I could study some, and perhaps even catch a little sleep.

After breaking out the books, time began to slip by rapidly as I focused on my studies.

Suddenly, around eight in the evening, there was a pounding on my door—not a knock but a loud *bang-bang-bang!* I almost jumped out of my skin. I learned later that would be the standard approach, beating loudly with a closed fist on the metal door, the sound echoing off the concrete walls.

I sprang up from the cot and hurriedly opened the door, expecting to see a couple of police officers holding on to a sick or injured prisoner in handcuffs. Instead, I was met by an officer with a broad smile on his face holding a plastic meal tray, similar to what one might see in the school cafeteria.

"Dinner, Doc?" the officer asked as he held out the tray toward me.

I glanced down to see what was on the menu for the night, which I soon learned was pretty much the same every night. In the larger "entrée" section of the tray were two pieces of bread with a slice of bologna and a slice of cheese. In one of the "side dish" squares was a pale whipped substance—either apple sauce or mashed potatoes—I wasn't sure which. And in another was a piece of lettuce with a slice of tomato. Finally, cut green beans (out of a can) filled the last square.

"No, thanks," I said without looking too long at the tray. I didn't want him to think I was turning up my nose at the facility's cuisine. "I appreciate the offer, though."

The officer continued his big smile and said, "OK," after which he turned and headed back down the narrow hallway, the metal door closing on its own.

Thankfully, I had brought some snacks to carry me through the shift. After seeing the special for the evening, I was glad I did.

As I sat back down on the bunk and listened to the footsteps of the officer going down the hallway, I thought about the fact that I hadn't heard any footsteps coming toward my room. I smiled, realizing this must be the way they welcomed all new "docs," tiptoeing down the hallway, suddenly and loudly banging on the door to scare the newbie, and then offering the evening's gourmet meal. I almost laughed out loud.

I stayed with the books until about two o'clock in the morning and then tried to sleep. I was tired after being up since six in the morning with a busy shift at the hospital before coming to the jail. I doubled up the pillow, laid on the bunk, and covered up with a thin gray blanket.

About an hour later, there was a loud noise outside the door that awakened me. I anticipated the loud *bang-bang-bang* but didn't yet hear it. There were several voices in the hallway, and then I heard another door open across the corridor from me. I hadn't thought to ask what was behind that door during my orientation. I listened closely to make out the conversation.

"Alright, Mr. Albert, sit right here." The voice appeared to be from a police officer talking to a prisoner. "Now let me explain what we would like for you to do," he continued.

A couple of minutes went by as the conversation rolled along. I determined that the room across from me must be the "breathalyzer room." The officer was trying to get the prisoner to blow into an open tube similar to a large straw, but the prisoner was apparently so intoxicated he couldn't hold his head up and blow into the device at the same time. I imagined his head in a state of constant bobbing and swaying as he tried to put his mouth over the tube. *I wonder how many tubes he sees,* I thought to myself with a smile.

The commotion went on for about thirty minutes before the officers decided it just wasn't going to work. I thought they might be coming to me next to draw blood for a blood alcohol level, but I would later learn that was not an approved process since I was only a medical student.

Eventually, I drifted off to sleep again, not being awakened until a little before six in the morning. The officer coming onto his morning shift at the jail was clearly a kind and considerate person. He knocked on the door rather than banging on it.

"Six o'clock, Doc. Shift's over," came the voice through the door.

"Thanks!" I replied, hopping up and starting to pack my gear. A few minutes later, I opened the door and headed down the hallway to the open intake area.

"Morning, Doc!" said the officer behind the large glass window, a smile on his face.

"Morning!" I replied, looking about to see if I needed someone to escort me out of the jail.

"Just hang a left, Doc, and I'll buzz you through," came the officer's voice from behind the glass, clearly reading my mind.

"Thanks!" I said as I followed his directions. Soon thereafter, I was riding the elevator down to the basement. *Wow, not a bad job!* I thought, reflecting on the fact that I hadn't had to do much, although I hadn't gotten much sleep either.

My mind jumped to my warm, comfy bed back at my small apartment.

I was glad I had signed up for the job.

During my next several shifts, I saw a few prisoners each night. None of their complaints were too challenging, and all had been able to wait for the clinic doc the following day.

My next shift would be different, however. It was a Saturday night with a fair number of folks receiving accommodations on the premises for an evening or two.

Bang-bang-bang! I shot straight up on the bunk and quickly stood and reached for the door. It was about two o'clock in the morning. I had been asleep in my scrubs with my tennis shoes on.

"Doc, we need you right away!" said the officer now in front of me, with a serious look of concern on his face and a few beads of perspiration on his forehead. "Follow me!" he said as he turned and started running down the hallway.

In the split second it took for me to turn and grab my bag off the desk, my mind began racing through the possibilities of what the urgent issue might be. Heart attack, passing out, severe abdominal pain, low blood sugar, acute blood loss, etc.—all the things I still felt anxious about trying to address on my own without any real resources.

I rapidly jogged down the hallway after the officer. The list of potentially serious conditions continued to pile up in my brain, now creating an anxious feeling in my stomach, accompanied by an intermittent wave of nausea.

As I entered the large intake area, multiple people were present and milling about. To my right, and closest to me, was a slender man of medium build in his thirties without a shirt on. An officer was standing next to him. I followed their gaze to what I presumed was my patient at the far end of the room.

There, a man was mostly lying on the floor, but with his head and shoulders propped up against the concrete block wall behind him.

An officer was squatting next to the man, who, like many other prisoners, was disheveled, wiry, and somewhat grimy in appearance. He looked to be in his fifties and had a medium-length, unkempt, and straggly beard and was wearing a long-sleeve plaid shirt over a dingy-appearing T-shirt. He wore an old pair of jeans with ragged and frayed tennis shoes.

As I briskly walked toward him, I looked for evidence of trauma but didn't note any blood, deformities, freshly torn clothing, etc. The obvious abnormality, which all could readily see, was a rhythmic jerking of the man's head simultaneous with a strong twitching of his right arm. He also had a milder degree of twitching that affected most of the rest of his body, all of which were concurrently occurring at a rate of about one to two jerking motions per second. His eyes were closed, his head was bowed away from the wall, and he did not appear to be responsive.

My mind eased just a little. I had seen this situation several times before. Even as a medical student—not yet a physician—I had a degree of familiarity and comfort in handling this type of scenario. Still, there was much left to consider. I was determined to not fall prey to overconfidence or "tunnel vision," where one too hastily locks in on a specific diagnosis to the exclusion of other possibilities.

As I approached the man on the smooth concrete floor, the officer who was stooped next to him turned to me and somewhat frantically said, "He just started having convulsions and fell to the floor!" It seemed as though the guard felt some degree of responsibility for this man's condition. Or perhaps he felt as though he should have seen it coming before the man fell down to the floor.

I squatted next to the prisoner, who continued to have rhythmical jerking of his bowed head and body. I was at the man's right side near his waist, about a foot from him. He lay mostly in a straight line perpendicular to the wall on which his shoulders were resting.

"Did he fall to the floor, or did he slide down the wall to this position?" I asked of the guard as I continued to observe the prisoner who was now my patient.

The officer seemed perplexed by my question. "Uh, he just kind of slowly went down the wall to the ground and started convulsing." The officer continued to have an anxious look on his face, which I could see out of the corner of my eye, as I kept my focus on the patient.

I reached out across the man's body to feel the pulse of his left arm, which was not twitching as prominently as his right arm. As I put my hand on his left wrist, the jerking of that arm became more forceful, staying in rhythm with the rest of his contractions. He had a strong pulse with a rate that I estimated to be about ninety to one hundred.

The patient also made some intermittent guttural noises from his throat as his head was slightly flexed forward with his head bobbing.

"Doc, aren't you gonna do something?" the officer next to me urgently asked, seemingly agitated by my lack of action.

"I just need to observe him," I said as I continued to keep my eyes on the patient. The officer who posed the question looked up to his supervisor, who was standing behind him and to my right. The supervisor didn't say anything, and I couldn't see whether he made any gestures or facial expressions.

I could tell tension was rapidly mounting in the room around me. There were now a couple of prisoners, several officers, a supervisor, and another officer behind the glass all watching the shaking man on the floor. And the "doc" next to the ill prisoner was an untested, new medical recruit who wasn't doing *anything* but watching the man. I knew the inaction was making them all uneasy, but at the moment, I felt comfortable with my initial assessment.

I opened my bag on the floor next to me, took out my penlight with my right hand, and carefully put my left hand on the prisoner's bobbing forehead. With some gentle pressure, I was able to move his head back toward the wall, attempting to fix his head between my hand and the wall. Although it continued to twitch, I was able to open one of his eyes with my thumb and shine my flashlight into it. At the time, he was looking straight ahead but quickly glanced in my direction and then forward again. I checked his other pupil. They both were briskly responsive to the light.

I let his head slowly come forward again, his eyes once again shut, the jerking of his head returning to full force. By now, about three or four minutes had gone by since my arrival on the scene. I remained kneeling next to the man at his right side, still watching him without making any comment to the officers there with me.

I knew they probably had concluded this was well beyond my ability to handle, and that I was totally lost. I could sense the tension escalating further.

Suddenly, the disheveled man lifted his head and turned it toward me, his shaking temporarily interrupted, especially at his head. He now opened both eyes, looked at me, and said in a tenor of disgust, "Dang, Doc, don't you know a seizure when you see one!"

He then abruptly closed his eyes, dropped his head forward again, and resumed his jerking and shaking, although the intensity of his activity seemed to be waning.

I looked at the officer who had chastised me for not doing anything and winked at him as I smiled. His face relaxed a little but still displayed a hint of confusion. I looked up at the supervisor, who was grinning from ear to ear.

Most likely, the supervisor had substantial experience with episodes like this and had probably seen real seizures during his time at the jail or elsewhere.

I now shared the man's diagnosis. "Well, Officer, our prisoner is having pseudoseizures," I said as I watched the disheveled man on the floor to see if he might respond to my comments. "There is no reason for concern, they are not real seizures." After a moment, I glanced from the patient to the officers around me and then back to the patient, wondering how long the older man would continue the masquerade.

"He may continue the shaking until he gets tired of doing it. He has complete control over it. There is no treatment necessary. He definitely does not require transportation to the hospital."

I then explained to the kneeling officer the clues from early on that helped me quickly realize the man was not having seizures. I walked him through some of the distinctions between real seizures and "fake" ones. I wrapped it up by telling him the most prominent telltale sign for this patient was the fact that the man talked in the middle of his "pretend" seizure. I explained that with a "grand mal" total-body seizure, the patient is unconscious, unresponsive, and cannot talk.

By this time, the prisoner on the floor had stopped his performance, either because he had developed fatigue or because the evidence against him had become overwhelming.

His attempt at deception had failed. His shaking had now miraculously dissipated.

However, he kept his eyes closed, perhaps hoping for our reconsideration. Or maybe he was trying to think up another disease witnessed during his time in jail or in the ER, which he had no doubt visited before. Certainly, he had recognized that an evening in a nice hospital was preferable to the accommodations at the jail.

"You can take him to his cell whenever you wish," I added as I stood up.

The officer who was squatting next to the patient now patted him on his left leg with his hand. "OK, Jimmy, the show's over, let's get up and get going." The officer looked over at me as he spoke to Jimmy, a smile now on his face: "No hospital for you this evening."

Jimmy, however, stayed motionless on the floor, his eyes still closed.

"Oh, one other thing, Officer," I said loudly as I started to head back to my station, ensuring Jimmy would hear me. "If he's too weak to get up and get to his cell, then he's probably too weak to eat, so you should hold his next meal. I wouldn't want him to choke on anything."

Following those words, Jimmy's recovery suddenly accelerated, with his strength rapidly returning. His eyes were now open, and he was getting up without assistance. I supposed that even if the jail's cuisine wasn't of a premier nature, for Jimmy, some cuisine that night was better than none!

A New Beginning

I worked my way through the corridors in the basement of the hospital. To some, it might have seemed like a barren, perhaps even gloomy, place. The walls were lined with pale-beige tiles, and the floor was cement. Other than the occasional sign pointing in the direction of one of the hospital's departments, the walls were featureless—no paintings, no posters, not even any graffiti. And at this early hour of the day, it was empty, devoid of any other people.

But it mattered not to me. I was in a cheerful and excited frame of mind. Today was my first day of being a "real doctor."

I had graduated from medical school in June of that year, officially becoming an MD. At that time, I didn't really feel any different. I was just glad that all the endless hours upon hours of study and routine patient care tasks—such as drawing blood, starting IVs, collecting various specimens for testing, cleaning and dressing wounds, inserting nasogastric tubes and urinary catheters, chasing lab results, documenting information, etc. were over (I mistakenly believed).

Now I felt it would be different. At twenty-five years of age, I was about to enter a phase in which I would be responsible for providing and overseeing patient care while still under the instruction and guidance of more experienced physicians. It was an exhilarating feeling to have completed that first long stage of the journey. But it was also a bit intimidating when reflecting upon the responsibility that now lay before me.

I knew that, at times, I would be engaged in battle with death itself, potentially saving one of its critically ill victims caught in the downward spiral of clinical deterioration. Now I would have the opportunity to help people in their time of need, particularly the poor, indigent, disenfranchised, afflicted, and the unfortunate.

I turned down the corridor where a sign overhead read "Emergency Department," with an arrow pointing down its hallway. This was the medical specialty I had chosen to pursue—emergency medicine.

In my medical school years, I had been drawn to the emergency room. It was there that the emergency medicine physician had to understand, retain, and utilize knowledge from almost all specialties in medicine, rather than narrowing one's focus to a singular field such as ophthalmology, orthopedics, pediatrics, etc. The spectrum of illnesses and injuries one might encounter was vast—heart attacks, gunshot wounds, drownings, heat stroke, asthma, sickle cell disease, rheumatoid arthritis, strokes, congenital heart disease, thyroid storm, women in labor, etc. The list seemed endless—and it was.

That is part of the excitement and the challenge of emergency medicine. However, it can also be anxiety producing. On any given shift, at any given time, any type of injury or illness could suddenly come through the doors to the emergency room and need immediate treatment. One had to be prepared for *everything*—in particular, those serious injuries or illnesses in which patients' lives were in the balance, and for which time was in short supply.

I went through another set of double doors that now brought me into the very large building where the emergency department was located. I continued down the drab and empty hallway until I reached the final set of double doors.

This was it! On the double doors before me, the sign read "Emergency Department—Rear Entrance." At last, I was about to begin my life as an emergency medicine physician. I paused for a moment, took a deep breath, mentally noted the moment, and then opened the door and walked through. Life would be different now—it would never be the same. The next important phase of the journey had begun.

My initial observation was that the emergency department at the prominent academic hospital was enormous, with hallways running in multiple directions. I would later recognize it was shaped like a giant rectangle, with rooms all around the outside and inside of the perimeter, and two major passageways that cut across the shorter width of the rectangle.

While the beige-colored tiles continued along the walls, they were now broken up by doors to rooms on each side of the wide corridors. Equipment such as IV poles, monitors, EKG machines, stands for trays, portable X-ray equipment, and other items were arranged along the sides of the hallways. Stretchers also lined a good portion of the walls, some of which were occupied by patients.

I walked down one of the longer corridors toward the front of the emergency department where I would meet the other physicians with whom I would be working that day. There were several patients lying on stretchers on each side ahead of me. *Busy place,* I thought as I walked along. It was only six in the morning, and already, the department was hopping.

As I approached the line of stretchers, I noticed a middle-aged man lying on the stretcher closest to me on my left, his head propped up slightly on the end of the stretcher facing toward me. He appeared somewhat disheveled and looked to be about forty-five to fifty years of age. He seemed to suffer from some form of chronic, wasting disease—perhaps alcoholism or drug use, based on his physical appearance. About the time my eyes fell upon him, he raised his head a little and noticed me walking down the hall toward him. I had on my midthigh-length white coat with a light-blue button-down shirt and a dark-blue tie. A folded stethoscope rested in my right coat pocket with various other instruments in my other pockets.

"Hey, Doc!" the man called out to me. I saw his eyes light up as his face gained expression. Before I could answer, he called out again "Hey, Doc!" He quickly sat up on the stretcher, better revealing the pale-blue-and-white patient gown covering his torso. It was as though his poor wasted body had gathered some energy upon seeing me approach him.

Now I really felt like a physician. In this new hospital system where I would be working for the next several years, patients seemed to have regard for the physicians and nurses who cared for them. You could see it in the way this man's eyes became alive when he noticed my impending presence. His salutation seemed to be one of warmth and gratitude.

I stopped at his bedside and took the outstretched hand he offered. This was what it was all about—caring for those in need. I looked into his weathered and wrinkled face that exhibited worn and weary eyes.

"Good morning, sir. My name is Dr. Grant. How can I help you?" My ears were now attuned to this man's needs, and I was prepared to listen closely to his concerns as he would relate them to me.

Without hesitation, he said to me, "Doc, you got a cigarette?" He held my hand tightly as he asked. I paused for a second before I could answer, not expecting the question.

"No, sir, I don't smoke," I responded, still waiting to hear him describe the symptoms of the ailment that had brought him to the hospital.

"Dang!" the man exclaimed as he threw my hand toward me and fell back against the stretcher with vigor. That wrinkled and worn face now displayed a broad scowl, demonstrating his strong dissatisfaction with my response.

He abruptly rolled over on his side, turning away from me to face the wall as he pulled the sheet up over his head while asking the rhetorical question, "Aren't you doctors good for anything?"

Thus went my first patient encounter in the wonderful profession and specialty I had chosen to pursue. The journey would prove to be an amazing expedition in which I would see, learn, and do more than I ever could imagine. It would broaden my perspective, teach me much, and change me in many ways. This day was only the initial step. I had received the first of many lessons to come in the incredibly unique world of emergency medicine!

Watch Out!

Dr. Allen was a beloved, knowledgeable physician, appreciated by all. He had served in the military and looked as though he were still on active duty as a Marine. His appearance was formidable. He had a shiny, mostly hairless head; a stocky build that made him look like a linebacker; and a decisive nature, as evidenced by his swift actions.

Despite Dr. Allen's tough-looking exterior, he was always a cheerful, upbeat, and engaging personality with seemingly boundless energy. He chose to see the world filled with opportunities and upsides, regardless of the challenges or difficulties one might encounter. He would always see the silver lining in the darkest of clouds. And, he had a warm, welcoming smile that suggested a softer side.

In our first year of training as residents, Dr. Allen would make use of every suitable situation to teach the young docs all he could, in the context of the patients we encountered during a given shift in the emergency room.

On this day, Dr. Allen was our faculty physician on shift and had just seen a patient himself. With a lull in patient flow at about nine thirty a.m. he walked through the emergency room rounding up first-year emergency medicine residents who were working the shift with him.

As I exited a patient room, I saw Dr. Allen walking briskly toward me. "Tom, come with me. I have a great thing to show you." He continued past me, not waiting for a response, anticipating my about-face to follow him. As I tried to catch up with him, he also picked up Mary and Bob, two other first-year residents in my class.

We all quickly fell in line like soldiers following their drill sergeant. Dr. Allen made a quick left turn into the lab room, a small enclosed area of the emergency department that contained equipment for running various tests like urinalysis, quick blood counts, blood sugars, and other "bedside tests." Dr. Allen walked in and put a glass slide on the microscope sitting on the counter, while the three of us stood at the doorway. He flipped on the light for the microscope, looked through its eyepieces, made a few adjustments, and then stood up and made his way past us out of the small room. He then encouraged us to enter.

We made our way in, trying not to step on each other's feet in such a compact space. Dr. Allen stood at the doorway and began to tell us about the patient's symptoms. We listened carefully, knowing that, at some point, Dr. Allen would want the information to start flowing the other way, asking our thoughts about the patient's complaints and exam findings. The goal was always to ensure we considered a spectrum of diseases, injuries, or conditions that might cause the patient's symptoms and physical exam findings.

Once the various diseases had been considered and added to the list of possibilities, one would begin to identify what additional information—in the form of questions to the patient, exam findings, testing, etc.—could help narrow down the list of possible diagnoses. Ideally, this would then lead one to a "working diagnosis" or "presumed diagnosis."

Dr. Allen informed us the twenty-two-year-old female presented to the emergency room with a chief complaint of itching, which had been going on for a couple of days. It was intense and localized in the lower abdominal and pubic area. Dr. Allen motioned with his hand that it was now our turn to ask questions, seeing if we could create the "differential diagnosis"—the list of possible diseases, injuries, or conditions that could cause this problem.

"Has she started using a new type of soap, shampoo, or lotion?" Mary asked, thinking this might be some sort of local allergic reaction. Dr. Allen smiled. "Excellent question! No, she has not," he replied. Dr. Allen loved to watch his young doctors think.

"New undies?" Bob asked, piggybacking on Mary's local allergic theory.

"Another excellent thought," Dr. Allen said, his eyes bright behind those round wire-rimmed glasses, his mouth smiling from ear to ear.

"Bug bites?" I asked, thinking about the intense itching the patient had described to Dr. Allen. I remembered my unfortunate past encounter with chiggers, a type of mite that lives outdoors and caused me to almost scratch my legs off. The itching had been exceedingly intense!

Dr. Allen's eyes gleamed even more brightly. "Ah, now you're getting close!" he said, the grin still wide on his face. He couldn't contain himself any longer. "*Pediculosis pubis*, to be exact," he declared. "Also known as 'pubic lice' or 'crabs.' The key is the intense itching along with its location. Nothing seems to itch like crabs. In fact"—Dr. Allen now raised one of his eyebrows for the next nugget of information—"I've had patients shave off all their pubic hair in an effort to get rid of them. I even had one person sit in a tub of alcohol for hours hoping it would kill them." Again, his broad smile.

Dr. Allen now leaned against the door to the tiny lab. "But to make the definitive diagnosis, you have to see one of them.

If you look closely at the pubic hair, you can sometimes see them hanging on to the base of the hair shaft, much like their cousins, *Pediculosis capitis*, or head lice." He glanced at the face of each of us to be sure his info was sinking in.

He now straightened up as he stood at the door, his arms behind his back and hands together, as if he were about to give orders to his platoon. "Now, I was able to get one of them off the patient and onto the microscope slide for you to see," he said, nodding toward the microscope on the counter. "Go ahead and take a look so you'll recognize it and be able to confirm the diagnosis in the future." Again, Dr. Allen nodded, this time looking at me since I was closest to the microscope. There wasn't enough space for us to easily change positions in the room, so I was first up.

I put my stethoscope into the back pocket of my scrubs and leaned forward, looking through the binocular eyepieces, adjusting the focus of the microscope as needed. But I could only see bright light, with no visible specimen on the slide. I toned down the light source but still couldn't bring anything into focus.

I flipped the microscope's objective lens to a lower magnification but still couldn't visualize an organism. I then leaned over and looked at the slide where it lay on the microscope stage, wondering if I could see any material with my naked eyes, in case I might need to reposition the slide.

"Dr. Allen," I said as I looked back through the eyepieces, "I don't see any lice." I was now adjusting both the coarse and fine focus, after which I took my eyes away from the eyepieces and looked again at the slide from the side.

I had noticed earlier that the slide did not have a coverslip on it, a thin piece of plastic or glass that goes on top of a specimen as it lies on the surface of the slide. Normally, one puts a coverslip on to keep specimens from moving. I wondered whether our critter had perhaps fallen or crawled off the slide.

"You don't?" Dr. Allen responded, seemingly confused about my statement.

After a pause, he suddenly uttered in an intense and frantic voice, "Oh, no!"

Hearing that tone of alarm in his words, I quickly looked in his direction, wondering why he had made that outburst. I didn't know if he had dropped something or if he suddenly had some sort of pain, or if he had forgotten to do something important.

He looked right at me, and with a worried, frightened appearance, exclaimed, "I forgot to tell you—they can jump really far!"

It was as if someone had pushed a button on a spring-loaded contraption that threw me backward against the wall of the tiny lab, separating me only about three feet from the microscope. I was rapidly brushing off the front of my scrubs as speedily as possible, my arms spinning like a Ferris wheel kicked into high gear. My feet were trying to climb the wall behind me in an effort to get further away from the slide Dr. Allen had placed on the microscope stage. In the flash of a split second, my mind pictured me in a tub of alcohol. *Yikes!*

Thankfully, both Mary and Bob had hastily stampeded out of the lab, almost running over Dr. Allen as he jumped out of their way. Once in the hallway, they, too, had begun to look like a whirring Ferris wheel with their arms moving at the speed of light.

It was only after I was able to rocket out of the lab also that I caught a glimpse of Dr. Allen, now doubled over in laughter, leaning back against the beige-tiled wall of the hallway just outside the lab. It took me a second to process his actions, subsequently realizing his microscope slide was a complete setup. There wasn't any *Pediculosis pubis* mite on that slide!

Several of the older residents peeked around the corner of the hallway to see what the commotion was about. They smiled and then returned to what they were doing.

Only later did I learn that this was an annual joke Dr. Allen loved to play on the incoming first-year residents in emergency medicine. In due time, we would indeed see pubic lice on patients presenting to the ER and confirm the diagnosis under the microscope. However, none of those mites had the Olympic leaping ability Dr. Allen had ascribed to them!

At times, emergency medicine can be gut-wrenching, soul-searching, frustrating, and even depressing. So, when rare occasions arise for humor or innocent fun as one works in the pressure cooker, it can be a welcome relief.

On that day, once my heart rate dropped back down below one hundred, I began looking forward to a future opportunity to even the score. I knew I would enjoy that day as much as Dr. Allen had this one.

Unanticipated

I could see him through the glass. His facial features were refined and distinguished, yet he had an overall hardy appearance. He was about five feet ten with a stocky build, and looked to be in his late forties. Most notable about him was the stylish but conservative dark-blue three-piece suit he wore, accented with a gold watch on his right wrist.

I was sitting in the small physician's office just off the main hallway of the psychiatric section of the ER. The upper half of the wall along the hallway was made of Plexiglas, allowing a view of patients as they entered the corridor leading to the psychiatric exam rooms.

The man stood at a fork in the hallway, with one route leading to the main ER and the other to the psychiatric area of the ER. The priest standing next to the man seemed to be uncertain about which direction to take.

As an emergency medicine resident, I would typically be working in the main ER. Now, however, I was working with the psychiatric residents and faculty during my month-long rotation in the psychiatric portion of the ER.

After a few moments of hesitation in the hallway, the priest turned to his left and entered the corridor into the psych area, the man walking slowly behind him. The priest held the man by the hand, talking with him as they made gradual progress toward the office. The Plexiglas and concrete wall kept their conversation private.

"Keith, it looks like we have a new patient," I said as the priest approached the office door with his companion. Keith was the senior psychiatric resident on duty and was in charge while the faculty psychiatrist was out to lunch.

Keith turned, looking over his shoulder as he put down the sandwich he had been eating. He swiveled his chair in the direction of the door to get up as others in the small office shifted their chairs to make room for him to walk. Space is a premium asset in every ER.

"Yes, Father, can I help you?" Keith asked as he opened the door. Except for the black cassock of the priest, Keith's appearance and mannerisms were very similar to the clergyman to whom he spoke. He had a dark beard and mustache, wire-rimmed glasses, a soft voice, and a reserved disposition.

"Yes, Doctor. Thank you." The priest paused for a moment before continuing softly. "This man came to my parish about an hour ago but has not spoken to me at all. It's as though he is in some kind of a trance." I could hear the conversation over Keith's shoulder. "I felt that something serious must be wrong, so I brought him here to see if you could help him. I've done all that I can, but I fear it is not nearly enough." A sense of urgency and sincere concern was evident in the priest's voice. No doubt he had tried to engage his companion in conversation, but to no avail.

"Thank you, Father," Keith said as he quickly scanned the hallway looking for open rooms. "Could you please walk him over to the room right behind you, Room 3, and we'll see him right away." Keith pointed to the room directly across from the office, only about ten feet away.

"And please leave the door open," Keith said as the priest turned to cross the hall with the well-dressed man.

Keith sat back down in his chair, picked up his sandwich with his right hand, and started writing with his left. Before taking a bite he spoke.

"Tom, why don't you go in and talk to our new patient and see what kind of story you get?" Keith continued writing as he took his next bite.

This was the typical approach. Junior psych residents or non-psych residents rotating through the psych ER would go see the patient first. That physician would attempt to determine the patient's problem and formulate a plan for the next steps in their evaluation. The assessment would then be discussed with the senior resident or faculty physician, who would return with the resident to examine the patient. The more senior psychiatrist would perform their own interview, allowing the junior resident to observe their approach and line of questioning.

In general, it was a good way of caring for patients while allowing physicians in training to further develop their skills. But this new patient seemed unlike all the other patients I had seen in the psych ER during my rotation. He looked like a troubled but successful executive rather than the more commonly encountered patients seen at an inner-city hospital—people with personality disorders, addictions, and various psychoses that made it difficult for them to integrate into society. I was afraid my inexperience with psychiatric interviews might negatively impact our distressed patient's state of mind.

"I would prefer not to, Keith," I said as I looked toward him. "This man looks like someone with unique emotional problems, and I wouldn't want to increase his burden through my lack of experience." I paused for a moment and then offered my suggestion. "If you don't mind, I'd rather you see him first while allowing me to observe your approach." As I finished speaking, Keith stopped writing and looked up at me.

Normally, a junior resident does whatever their senior resident asks of them, but psych folks don't fit that mold. If one is firm in their conviction when making a reasonable request, the psych residents and faculty usually go with the flow.

"OK, Tom, give me a minute and we'll go see him together." I sighed with relief. Keith finished the last two bites of his sandwich, and we headed across the hall.

As we entered the room, the priest excused himself and left us with the patient. Ignoring our presence, the man remained standing and began to pace back and forth in the small room. As he made a turn toward us, Keith held out his hand and spoke to him. "Hello, my name is Dr. Harris and this is Dr. Grant." The man stopped, looked coldly at Keith, then at his extended hand, and then to me. He put his head back down and returned to his slow and deliberate pacing.

The room was only about ten feet by eight feet, so he didn't have far to travel in his steps. His stride was very short as he slowly but precisely crossed the small room. He seemed to be lost in his thoughts, perhaps engaged in an internal conversation of his own.

After the man's initial rejection of Keith's introduction, we began the process of closing the wide door to the room to give us privacy for our conversation. Since the door opened into the room, it was necessary to first move the two chairs for Keith and me out of the door's path and then put them back against the door once it was closed. A small couch was on the wall opposite the door, providing only a few feet between patient and physicians.

"Sir, can you tell us your name?" Keith asked as he motioned for the man to sit down on the couch. The man paused, visually inspecting each of us again, and then sat down without speaking. He clasped his hands together, leaned forward, placed his forearms on his knees, and looked down at the floor.

Keith and I sat down in the chairs against the door, directly across from our patient, providing minimally adequate space between us and the troubled man.

"Sir, can you please tell us your name?" Keith asked again. "We would like to see if we can help you." The man said nothing in response, but after several moments, he raised his head and looked straight ahead. His stare was distant as if he were looking out over a landscape. After about twenty seconds, he looked down again to the floor. Soon thereafter, he uttered a low moan and slightly shook his head from side to side.

As Keith and I patiently waited for any remark the man might wish to offer, I visually assessed him. He looked as though he might have just walked out of a Fortune 500 business meeting. His sandy-blond hair was combed neatly to one side, and his face was clean shaven. He wore a finely tailored white shirt with a conservative silk tie. His suit was also conservative, made of fine-quality wool, and probably cost more than my monthly income as a resident. His socks were thin and appeared expensive, and his shoes were black leather—clean and brightly polished. The scent of his aftershave had begun to fill the room with a pleasant aroma.

As the man stared straight ahead again, he took a pressed monogrammed white handkerchief from his inner coat pocket. He wiped his forehead, which had no visible perspiration.

Keith noticed the monogram. "That *M* on your handkerchief, does that stand for Michael?" It was a clever effort by Keith to try a different method of engagement.

The man finished wiping his forehead and placed it back into his pocket. He continued to look straight ahead without speaking as if he were continuing his internal debate.

I looked over at Keith, who turned to look at me. The question in my mind was: *What do you do now?* Before Keith could read my mind and provide an answer, our patient responded.

"Mike." He spoke only the single word. Then, after a brief pause, he repeated it: "Mike." He again looked straight ahead.

This slow, piecemeal task of trying to gain information and generate the beginning of a conversation went on for about fifteen minutes. We had learned little because our patient had spoken little, and not much of what our patient said was in response to our questions. Rather, Mike seemed to be in deep thought, which he occasionally verbalized in barely audible fragments.

By the half-hour mark, the only other information we had gained was a collection of brief comments: "I can't stand it anymore, I just can't take it. All that killing—I can't do it anymore. Fire, people burning, dying."

At one point, Mike abruptly and very deftly reached out and grabbed my left pant leg before I could even react. The speed with which he moved was impressive, and a little scary. He held the cuff for a second or two, looking at a small stain, and then blurted out the word "blood." He followed that with an intense look that sent shivers up and down my spine. His eyes were ice cold and piercing.

Suddenly, there was a brief knock on the door, which cracked open very slightly, bumping against our chairs. "Keith, you've got a long-distance call that sounds important." The door then rapidly and quietly closed behind us. We exchanged glances and began the furniture shuffle that would allow us to get out.

As Keith was about to step out of the room, he turned back toward me. "See if you can make any progress, and I'll be back in a minute," he whispered. He took another step and looked back at me again before the door closed, adding, "I think he's a vet." I repeated the furniture shuffle and settled back into my chair, feeling inadequate and uncomfortable about the task before me.

I had come to the same conclusion Keith had—this gentleman must be a veteran. I thought he may have been a fighter pilot, perhaps dropping napalm on a village and having witnessed too much of the inhumanity of war. I imagined he might be tormented by frequent remembrances of the horrors he had experienced, perhaps reaching a breaking point—post-traumatic stress disorder, in today's terms.

I continued the effort to try to establish some meaningful communication with Mike but was unable to make any progress. Then Mike unexpectedly stood up and started to slowly pace again across the room to my left. I hoped this activity would finally precede the opening of a conversation. But instead, Mike muttered the same phrases again and again, revealing nothing new.

Then, abruptly, he stopped near the center of the room, only about four or five feet from me. He was standing oblique to me, such that I could see part of his left side, a partial profile of his face, and most of his back. He looked straight ahead at the blank wall and spoke.

"I'm done." While concerning, that brief statement didn't alarm me at first. Then, I saw his right hand quickly and smoothly slide inside his coat, reaching to the small of his back. His motion was incredibly fast and effortless as if he had done it many times before. In that fraction of a second, my mind rapidly processed all the information I'd collected since the first moment I had seen him. I realized he was reaching for a gun, probably intending to kill both himself and me.

My mind inaudibly screamed in panic, but the thought vanished in the same instant it appeared. It's remarkable how the brain can think so logically and swiftly when faced with a potentially life-threatening situation. Time seemed to have almost stopped, a perception fueled by the huge surge of adrenaline accelerating my thoughts as they zipped across the millions of synapses in my brain.

Intellectually, I quickly but calmly considered the options: (1) I could try to get out of the room before he started shooting. I immediately dismissed that one. I knew I wouldn't even be able to stand up before he could start firing. (2) I could go for the guy and his gun. He was very stocky and powerfully built, and his reflexes were lightning quick. I knew there was very little to no chance I could get the gun away from him. And if I pounced on him, he would see that as an attack, which would give him reason to kill me if he hadn't intended to do so beforehand. (3) I could sit comfortably in my chair and die in peace.

My mind selected the third option as being the most logical, although quite a few of my neurons were zealously objecting.

My eyes intently followed Mike's actions as my brain continued to process time in slow motion. Mike began to withdraw his hand from inside his coat at the small of his back, but then he paused.

He spoke—almost inaudibly—as he hesitated. "Gone…"

I tried to rapidly assimilate that word in the context of all the other information as I kept my eyes fixed on his right hand as it now began to come out from underneath his coat. I was momentarily stunned—I did not expect what I saw.

His hand was empty!

In that instant, at the speed of light, my mind hastily reassessed the situation. It readily locked onto the previous option number one—get out as fast as I could, not knowing whether he was carrying his gun in a different location today or whether he might have some other weapon. The ensuing furniture shuffle was no longer a shuffle but rather an explosion with chairs almost flying through the air. I was out in a flash.

Security and police were immediately called, and they responded instantaneously. After a brief conversation with us and with weapons at the ready, the lead officer spoke to Mike through the closed door, letting him know they would be opening the door to enter the room.

Once they gained visual contact with Mike, and upon seeing the absence of weapons in his hands or in the room, they cautiously entered. They carefully explained to Mike in a nonthreatening voice each action they were about to take as they approached him, after which they patted him down for weapons. Of course, that was a little late in our overall patient assessment process, but nonetheless, it was greatly appreciated!

Mike was admitted to a secure area on the psychiatric floor of the hospital.

After a couple of more days in the psychiatric section of the ER, it was time for me to rotate out and back to the main ED. I intermittently checked back with the psychiatric staff to see how Mike was doing.

It was determined that Mike indeed had severe psychiatric sequelae from certain events in his past, and he was a veteran of the Vietnam War. In my last discussion with the psychiatric staff, they were exploring the possibility of whether Mike had become a professional killer after the war, a situation that might have exacerbated his mental anguish and ultimately led to his psychotic break.

In the years that followed, my mind would occasionally, and unpredictably, replay those last few moments of my lone interview with Mike. I often wondered why he might have left his gun at home that day.

Perhaps he knew he would seek out a priest for help and could not bring himself to enter a house of worship with a gun. Or maybe he saw the weapon as a symbol of a path he could no longer tread, and chose to separate himself from it that day. Or perhaps the Lord was looking out for all of us in the psychiatric ER on that day. In any case, I am thankful to God for Mike's pivotal decision that affected all our lives.

~ ~ ~

It's hard to know what some people suffer with in their mind. They may carry great pain or regret for extended periods of time in their lives. That anguish can be a burden that progressively drains them of their energy and their desire for life. Some may even reach the point where ending their life becomes the best-perceived solution for the pain they suffer.

Unfortunately, too often, there is no clearly visible clue that provides insight into a person's state of mind—no window to see their suffering until it may be too late to help them.

We wince when we see the horribly broken leg or the gaping wound to one's body. And we immediately empathize with the pain that person must be experiencing. If we could only see in a similar fashion the injury or illness some people suffer in their minds, perhaps we could help ease their pain and offer some degree of relief from the distress they experience.

I am grateful for the psychiatrists and other mental health professionals who are committed to helping those in our society who suffer with mental illness. As we gain greater and greater understanding of the science behind many of these illnesses, it offers substantial hope for the treatment of mental health conditions in the future.

I hope and pray that our treatment for mental illness can soon experience the progress and breakthroughs that have occurred in other areas of medicine.

Lessons Learned

Julie came rushing around the corner of the hallway, frantically pushing the stretcher as fast as she could. My initial reaction was that she should slow down before she hurt someone. Then it became clear she was navigating the stretcher toward one of the major resuscitation rooms.

The words she cried out immediately clarified the reason for her haste.

"He's arrested!" she shouted as she swung the stretcher past the last corner and rapidly guided it into Major Resuscitation Room 2, where equipment was ready to treat critically ill or injured patients.

I was a second-year resident in the emergency medicine residency program, which prepared physicians for the broad scope of illnesses and injuries one might encounter as a physician, sometimes in sudden fashion—like this patient.

A handful of clinicians sprang toward the resuscitation room, hurriedly following Julie and the stretcher into the room. She swiftly locked the wheels as it came to rest in the center of the room, providing ample space around the stretcher for multiple medical personnel to access the patient simultaneously.

The primary hospital for our emergency medicine residency program was a high-volume facility that saw close to a hundred thousand patients a year in the emergency department. The department was staffed 24/7/365 with first-, second-, and third-year residents, each of whom had varying degrees of knowledge and experience. In addition, for every shift in the ED, a proficient faculty physician was present to oversee the residents as they provided patient care. The faculty physician that evening was the most brilliant and skilled physician I would ever know.

As the handful of doctors and nurses entered the room, the faculty physician, Dr. Bill Rogers, walked up next to me and said, "Tom, you take the lead."

Those words meant I was to fill the role of team lead, an assignment needed on every critically ill patient. Such patients require many decisions and actions in a very compressed time frame to sustain life or, as in this patient's case, to try to bring them back to life after sudden death.

Typically, the team lead for this type of patient scenario would be the third-year emergency medicine resident. However, as Julie raced our patient, Mr. Cantwell, into Major Resuscitation Room 2, the third-year resident was already busily caring for another seriously ill patient.

I had not yet filled this role in my training, but I knew Dr. Rogers would be at my side the whole time. I had seen him nurture, educate, nudge, redirect, and refocus—as needed—a number of other residents in critical care cases. Bill seemed to always be several steps ahead, continually processing information as it flowed to the team leader while watching everything that happened in the room.

If a potential mistake in decision-making was brewing, Bill would gently but firmly intervene in a kind and thoughtful way to help the person recognize a better or more appropriate approach. He was an incredibly knowledgeable, experienced, and gifted physician.

And he was extremely cool under fire—I never saw him get rattled, even in the face of some horrific patient scenarios. If I failed somewhere along the way, our patient would still receive the highest quality of care without delay because of Bill's presence.

Still, a tempest of emotion swept over me as I stepped to Mr. Cantwell's right side to quickly assess him. I was now primarily responsible for orchestrating and providing the necessary care for a patient with sudden death. Every second counted. Every decision was critical.

Cardiac arrest is one of the most challenging areas of medicine. Although heart disease is the most frequent cause of cardiac arrest, there are many other causes—some of which can be readily treated if identified promptly.

Failure to recognize one of those other conditions would substantially decrease Mr. Cantwell's chance of survival. While TV series often show the patient surviving without any serious deficits afterward, the reality is that most people do not survive cardiac arrest, and many who do survive often suffer serious complications.

However, those disappointing statistics are due, in part, to the time interval between when a person collapses from cardiac arrest and when they receive basic and advanced treatment, including CPR. Additionally, the underlying reason for the cardiac arrest is a very important factor in survival.

Knowing the patient's life is in the balance with a myriad of possible causes for their arrest, and having no knowledge about their prior medical problems, generates a high degree of anxiety and intense pressure. Yet, this is what I—and other EM residents—were being trained to handle. It requires a logical, intellectual, and unemotional approach in a very compacted time frame.

I announced my role as team lead to those in the room, thereby identifying myself as the individual to whom all information was to flow. I was to be the source of data interpretation, decisions, and orders while overseeing and orchestrating the rapid and multifaceted care of the patient.

Julie, who was already starting an IV in Mr. Cantwell's right arm, briefly looked up at me and smiled for a split second, which I took as a vote of confidence. She was a wonderfully capable and compassionate nurse—someone you would want caring for you if you were critically ill.

The team was already engaged in all the necessary procedures—ventilating the patient with 100 percent oxygen while preparing for intubation, gaining IV access for drug administration, charging the defibrillator paddles should we need to shock the patient, applying the EKG pads, drawing the necessary blood to send for lab tests, and undressing the patient so we could visually gain as much information as possible—such as scars from prior surgeries, medication patches, unrecognized trauma or wounds, or medical ID bracelets or necklaces.

Standing next to the wall at the foot end of the stretcher, one of the clerks was hurriedly going through Mr. Cantwell's pants pockets looking for prescription bottles, medical cards, or any other clues that might be helpful as treatment began.

It was a beehive of activity.

As Julie taped down the IV to Mr. Cantwell's arm, she provided the limited amount of information he had given her just before his arrest. He had complained of indigestion and came to the ED to see if he could get some antacids to treat his heartburn.

This type of discomfort is sometimes associated with heart attacks. Even in today's world where it's well known, people still have a tendency to deny the potential seriousness of the symptom. However, Mr. Cantwell's visit to the ED for his heartburn had given him the best chance of survival following his arrest in the emergency department.

Although his history strongly suggested heart disease as the cause of his arrest, my quick initial exam also looked for evidence of other potential causes—recent trauma, blood clots, lung disease, drug use, overdose, kidney failure, and other diseases.

When the first EKG strip came off the machine, it was clear Mr. Cantwell was in ventricular fibrillation, a heart condition in which there is no organized electrical heart activity and therefore no forward blood flow, resulting in Mr. Cantwell's unconscious and pulseless state. The ongoing chest compressions were an effort to provide that forward blood flow until his heart rhythm could be reestablished.

I instructed the waiting first-year resident to deliver the electrical shock from the defibrillator, attempting to "reset" the naturally occurring electrical pacemaker in Mr. Cantwell's heart. If the pacemaker could be restarted in an organized fashion, it would begin pumping blood to all his other organs. With such a short time period between his arrest and the delivery of the shock, the hope was that he would quickly regain function.

Later in my career, I would have patients arrest right in front of me while talking to me, and after rapidly administering a defibrillation shock to them, it would reset their heart rhythm and they would literally finish speaking the sentence they were in the middle of when they arrested.

Unfortunately, this was not Mr. Cantwell's initial response.

We followed the first defibrillation with others, interspersed over time with a variety of different intravenous drugs. At times, we briefly reestablished a heart rhythm that could generate forward blood flow, but it would then suddenly deteriorate to the chaotic and unorganized rhythm of ventricular fibrillation.

With all the procedures completed except for the intermittent drug administration and electrical defibrillations, all eyes fixed upon the cardiac monitor on the wall above the head of the bed. I was constantly feeling for the presence or absence of a pulse after each intervention.

Time was our enemy. The longer it took Mr. Cantwell to develop a stable, organized, and perfusing heart rhythm, the less chance for his survival. It seemed as though Mr. Cantwell's heart was going through every type of heart rhythm I had ever encountered in my studies and my clinical experience. We were in a rapidly repeating cycle of quick stabilization followed by sudden deterioration.

After more than an hour of effort, Mr. Cantwell's heart rhythm returned to asystole, also known as flat line. However, this time, no drug could coax any heart rhythm to appear.

There was no additional therapy to offer. I racked my brain for any other option to try, anything that might bring Mr. Cantwell back to us. At that moment, I felt Bill's hand on my shoulder. I had become so fixated on the battle of heart rhythms, I had become less aware of his presence in the room.

"You gave him every chance," he said. "There's nothing else we can offer." He patted me on the back and headed toward the door. He knew it was over.

Julie probably saw the anguish on my face. I was stunned. With all the knowledge of how to treat the various cardiac disturbances Mr. Cantwell had suffered, and with a great team of competent and skilled providers, and with the advantage of having started treatment within just a couple of minutes of his cardiac arrest, we had failed to save him.

I had failed to save him.

"I will see if he has any family here," Julie said as she, too, left the room with others who had collectively attempted to save Mr. Cantwell's life. I remained alone at the head of the bed, replaying all the steps, all the heart rhythms, all the procedures, all the drugs. What could I have done differently? What could I have missed? I was at a loss.

It wasn't supposed to work this way. We did everything "right." Why couldn't we save this man? I was devastated. I felt as though I had let this man die. He had come to the ED for medical help. I was there to help him, but I had failed. Silence surrounded me. I looked around the empty room. I looked at Mr. Cantwell lying on the stretcher. It was over. It was final. Death had claimed him. There was nothing else that could be done.

I had witnessed death before, but this was *my* patient. I had made all the decisions regarding his care. I had considered all the possible causes for his condition. I had orchestrated his treatment.

I had failed to save Mr. Cantwell.

My eyes watered as I continued to reflect. The housekeeping personnel came in to begin cleaning the room so it would be ready for the next patient that might be in need of its resources. The nurses would return and prepare to take Mr. Cantwell to the morgue after checking to see if the family was present and wanted to see him. I would speak with them right away if they had accompanied him to the hospital.

I slowly walked out of the room to one of the long countertops against the wall opposite Major Resuscitation Room 2 and sat down. I had Mr. Cantwell's chart in my hand, a clipboard filled with documents related to his ER visit.

I flipped to the nurses' notes, reviewing each of Mr. Cantwell's heart rhythms that were recorded, along with each drug administered, and all the procedures that were performed. Every item had a time stamp noted next to it. It was a written replay of all that had transpired during the resuscitation. As I went through the documentation, I searched for something that I could have done differently—anything that could have changed Mr. Cantwell's outcome. But I could not find it.

As the team lead, I needed to write the physician's note in Mr. Cantwell's medical record, but I couldn't. I leaned forward with my elbows on the desk and my head in my hands, staring at the pale-gray glazed tiles on the wall. I continued to wonder where I must have gone wrong. Surely, there had to be something else I could have done, something that would have made a difference.

I was lost in a vast desert of emptiness and loneliness. As I mentally wandered in that wasteland, mindlessly looking at the wall in front of me, I felt a hand on my shoulder. A soft, familiar voice whispered in my ear. I recognized it as Mrs. Edwards, one of the elderly cleaning ladies who had been in Mr. Cantwell's room.

"I know you cared for him," she said sincerely, briefly pausing before she continued. "I know you did everything you could to save him. You're a good doctor."

I put my hand on hers as it still rested on my shoulder and thanked her for her kind words. I could feel tears welling up in my eyes.

I have no doubt she had seen this situation other times in her years of work at the hospital. She had probably witnessed other doctors who thought that if they studied and worked hard enough, they could battle any life-threatening disease and come out victorious—they could save their patients when their lives hung in the balance. But then they faced the harsh reality. Doctors can't make everyone better. You work hard to prepare and you do the best you can do. That's all you can offer your patients. You are a doctor, not a savior.

It was one of the most powerful, painful, and necessary lessons for me to learn as a physician. Becoming a doctor is about much more than just learning about diseases and their treatments. There is also much to learn about life, about people, and about oneself.

The brief but kind words of the elderly housekeeping woman, and her recognition and desire to ease my suffering, helped me to heal from the pain of that day—from the loss of Mr. Cantwell. On that day, she had been my physician, providing wonderfully kind and compassionate care, offering me the type of medicine I needed at the right time. I will always be indebted to her for her thoughtfulness and concern, and the excellent care she provided me.

Malice

It was an early Friday afternoon and the ER was exceptionally busy already. Only one or two rooms had yet to be occupied by incoming patients.

The hectic pace was not just related to the number of patients coming into the ER, but also to the seriousness of their illness or injury. The sicker the patient, the more time and resources required for their care. Such was the case that afternoon, with a number of patients already awaiting admission into the hospital.

In addition to the three ER physicians working in the emergency department that afternoon, there were a number of admitting physicians—doctors who would be caring for seriously ill patients after their admission into the hospital from the ED.

"Ma'am, can you tell me when your abdominal pain first began and what it felt like initially?" Mrs. Jackson, my patient, was lying on the stretcher in Room 6, with the head of the stretcher elevated about thirty degrees to make her more comfortable. She was in her midforties and did not appear to be in any serious pain or distress.

Before she answered my question, a sudden scream came from down the hallway. I immediately recognized it as different from the occasional wail or outcry from a patient in pain or grief, or someone experiencing a psychotic break. This was a shriek, as if the person were suddenly and terribly frightened. That impression was rapidly confirmed by the cry for help that followed.

I jumped up from the stool and dashed out of Room 6, looking down each side of the hallway, uncertain as to where the scream had come from. There was the usual background noise of voices, equipment, device alarms, and doors opening and closing. But when the cry "Help!" was repeated, I could tell it came from the far end of the hallway to my right. As I started running toward it, I had an uneasy feeling about what I would find.

That discomfort intensified as I reached the open door to the room, slowing down to make the abrupt ninety-degree turn from the hallway into the room. My mind momentarily froze as it attempted to process what I saw.

Across the room, near the far wall, was a male patient in a sitting position on an older type of metal stretcher. The flat bed portion of the stretcher was a little higher than three feet off the ground. The man was leaning out over the raised metal bed rail on the right side of the stretcher. His chest was clothed in a sleeveless white T-shirt, and a white sheet covered his legs. He appeared to be in his twenties, and about five foot ten with a slight but muscular build.

At the right side of the stretcher stood Kala, one of the ER nurses. Her short, petite body was facing the stretcher with both of her arms raised above her head. Her hands were wrapped tightly around the man's right wrist, his arm extended in the air toward her head as he leaned over the bed rail. A look of fright was on her face as she struggled to hold on to the man's arm, which was slowly being forced closer to her. In his left hand, he held a fistful of Kala's blouse at her right shoulder, keeping her from escaping his grasp.

In that first fraction of a second, I saw a glint of light flash from the man's right hand, revealing the polished, four-inch steel knife blade, pointing downward at Kala as she struggled to keep it from her body.

He clearly had the physical advantage as he forced the knife closer to her head. Fear must have endowed Kala with tremendous strength to resist him, even as she was slowly losing the battle.

Having braked as I turned the corner, I now accelerated into the room. Reaching Kala's side, I grabbed the man's arm with both hands just below where Kala's were doing the same. I was amazed at how strong he was—much more than I anticipated from his size.

Kala was able to pull herself free from the grip of the man's left hand and fell backward into a chair against the wall.

"Get out!" I emphatically shouted at her, quickly realizing this would not be an easy battle. The man was now almost on his knees on the elevated stretcher, with a wild look in his eyes. He seemed intent upon knifing someone in his agitated state of mind. And in the brief time span since my arrival no other reinforcements had yet appeared.

Kala paused, not wanting to leave me in the situation she had just been freed from.

"Go!" I shouted again as I struggled with the man, uncertain where this would lead in the next few moments. Kala ran for the door. I knew she would return with help.

Concern for my own safety now summoned that extra measure of strength Kala had demonstrated. That surge gave me confidence that I could gain the upper hand against the attacker. My fear diminished as my determination increased.

I knew I outweighed the man by at least twenty or thirty pounds, but more importantly, he was in a semi-sitting position while I was standing, although our heads were at the same height. I was able to push his arm backward away from me even though he had grabbed my right arm with his free left hand and dug his prominent fingernails deep into my flesh.

"Drop the knife!" I yelled, looking intently into his eyes. "Drop the knife!" I hoped he would recognize this as a losing battle and give up the fight.

Rather than following my command, however, the man intensified his effort. Yet I was able to continue pushing his knife-wielding arm back toward his body, forcing him lower onto the stretcher, weakening the leverage he initially had. I was now the one leaning against the raised bed rail on the right side of the stretcher.

As I gained more of an advantage, he still did not give up. Instead, he adjusted his strategy, flexing his head forward as he attempted to sink his teeth into my right wrist, but wasn't quite able to reach it. I leaned harder over the bed rail, trying to pin him against the stretcher with my forearm, countering his new threat.

Then, he momentarily dropped his head back against the stretcher and attempted to slide his body toward the foot end of the stretcher to get into a better position to bite me. But that approach resulted in my forearm being close to his neck.

I continued to yell at him to drop the knife as I now began to apply pressure against his neck.

Still, he was not dissuaded. He began thrusting his knee toward my head. I knew he must have street drugs on board to give him this degree of strength, persistence, and intent to do harm.

Thankfully, at that point, the cavalry arrived—a security officer and another physician. The security officer immediately went for the knife arm, adding one of his hands to mine while using his other hand to pry the knife from the man's hand. The arriving physician launched his upper body onto the top of the man's lower legs, pinning them to the stretcher so he could no longer kick with his knees.

Two police officers immediately followed, further taking control of the situation and eventually handcuffing the man. The battle was over—or, at least, I thought so.

No longer needed, I left the room and searched for Kala, grabbing some antiseptic wipes to clean the fingernail wounds on my forearm. I imagined she had been severely traumatized by the surprise attack, recognizing she could have been killed or seriously injured.

I found her in the nurses' office sitting in a chair and being consoled by several of the nurses. She had tears in her eyes, no doubt thinking about what could have happened, and how it could have affected her life.

I knelt down next to the chair. "Are you OK?" I asked, not knowing what else to say. She nodded in affirmation. "Are you hurt anywhere?"

"No, I'm fine," was her reply. She offered a weak smile that must have taken a significant amount of composure with the assault so fresh in her mind.

"You are one tough cookie," I said, speaking from my heart, my mind replaying the image I had first seen when I arrived at the room. For a second time, I was in disbelief she was able to hold off the man's violent attack on her.

"Amen to that," the charge nurse for the shift added, gently patting Kala on the back as the other nurses surrounded her.

I wanted to ask how the situation unfolded, but I knew Kala must have already told the story to those in the room, and I didn't want to make her relive it again. I knew I would find out later. After pausing for a minute, not knowing what else to say, I tried to lighten the mood with a request.

"Would you do me a favor?" I asked, Kala nodding her head up and down in response.

"If you enter any of the arm-wrestling contests at the local establishments around here, please let me know. I would really like to make some money by placing a bet on you to win." I gave it my best smile and briefly saw a twinkle in her eye and a slight grin of her own.

Knowing that Kala was in good hands and doing well under the circumstances, I left the nurses' office to get back into the flow of patient care. First I located some Band-Aids to cover the crescent-shaped wounds on my forearm. Then I found the chart for Mrs. Jackson, the patient I had been talking with before the crisis, and began writing a brief note on it.

Jenny and Mary, two of the nurses who had been in the office with Kala, walked by the desk having exited the room as others went in to check on Kala. They were discussing details of the crisis. I hated to interrupt, but I wanted to understand the reason, if any, for the attack.

"Excuse me, ladies, did either of you hear how the incident in Room 13 began?" I asked, after waiting for a pause in their conversation.

"It won't make sense, and it's hard to believe, but here's what happened," Jenny said as she and Mary both turned toward me.

"The patient came in complaining of terrible pain in his back and abdomen. Dr. Joiner saw him and thought he had a sickle cell crisis based on his past history of similar bouts, so he followed the protocol and started an IV, gave him pain meds, and put him on oxygen." Jenny had an intense look on her face as she described the events.

"Dr. Joiner had requested the patient's old chart, which came at about the same time as the results for the blood work he had ordered. Neither supported the story the patient had told him, so Dr. Joiner went in to examine the patient again and reassess his pain." Jenny paused, and Mary, who seemed to be on the same wavelength, picked up the narrative.

"When Dr. Joiner went in, the man was sleeping. He awakened the patient, who immediately began complaining about his terrible pain and asked for more pain medicine. Dr. Joiner told him he had his old chart with all his previous visits to the ER and the man did not, in fact, have sickle cell disease." Mary's eyes widened some as she described what happened next.

"He told the patient he saw in his chart where the doctors had previously counseled him about his drug-seeking behavior multiple times." Mary paused as she caught her breath, with Jenny nodding in affirmation of Mary's description of the events.

"Dr. Joiner told the man he would not receive any more pain medicine, and they would flag his record in the computer to prevent the man from deceiving others with his story. At that point, the man started cursing Dr. Joiner, who said they would be removing his IV and sending him home."

Jenny now picked up the thread. "Dr. Joiner wrote an order on the chart to discontinue the man's IV and discharge him. Kala picked up the chart a little later and went into the room to carry out the orders. The man had fallen back asleep, and Kala woke him up to let him know she was taking out his IV. She didn't see him pull out the knife until she turned toward him just as he was about to stab her."

They both paused at this point, no doubt putting themselves in the situation Kala faced, wondering how they would have responded and whether they could have reacted in time—as Kala did.

"I can't imagine how frightening that must have been," Mary said as she looked from me to Jenny while shaking her head from side to side, her ponytail swishing behind her head.

"I'm just glad you heard her scream," said Jenny. "With all the background racket and commotion, and that room being in the far corner of the hallway, those who did hear it probably just thought it was a patient in pain."

At that point in the conversation, I heard a sudden noise coming from the direction of the room where the brief battle had occurred. I looked up to see the man, now with handcuffs and ankle bracelets on, standing in the doorway to the room, flanked on each side by a police officer.

They each had one hand in his armpit closest to them as he walked, no doubt to keep him from falling, but also to be sure he didn't attempt any aggressive acts on his way out. His chains were jingling as he moved.

I was standing at a counter in the hallway that led from that room to the ER exit. Mary and Jenny headed off to look after patients as I shifted my attention. The man slowly began to shuffle in my direction when he suddenly recognized me and started nodding his head as he kept his eyes fixed on me. When he got closer he spoke.

"It ain't over," he said as he kept nodding his head, acting as though he were in control of the situation. "I know where you are," he continued, still nodding in affirmation of the words he spoke as if it added a degree of prophetic impact.

I looked at him, not expressing any emotion and not responding. But what he said next did catch my attention.

"I'll be watching for you," he said with a smile on his face as he raised his cuffed right hand, pointing his index finger at me with his thumb upturned and his three other fingers curled into his hand, simulating a gun. Then he dropped his thumb down to his index finger and mouthed, "Pow!" He followed his animation with a broad grin.

Up to that point, I had thought of his threats in the context of a physical confrontation, maybe with his knife again. Although concerning, I foolishly thought I could just avoid him if I were careful and watchful. And security at the hospital was pretty sound.

The possibility of being shot at was a whole different world of concern, however. No matter how careful I might be, he could fire a shot before I ever saw him. That was unnerving.

I watched as he continued to shuffle his chained lower legs toward the ER exit, the officers walking next to him with a tight grip on each of his arms. They kept him facing forward, even as he struggled to turn his head back toward me, no doubt wanting to reiterate or build upon his threat.

When I returned for my next shift, my concern escalated significantly. The security officer who had responded to the threat the previous day called the ER to let me know the prisoner had made bail and was now out of jail. Having witnessed the man's threat as he was leaving the ER, the officer suggested I change my routine and my points of entry and exit from the hospital for each shift—just to be safe.

Despite my desire to not be intimidated, I thought it wise to listen to the officer's suggestion. For the next several months, I changed my times for arriving and departing and I entered and exited through a variety of different locations, intently aware of my surroundings.

Thankfully, I did not encounter the aggressive young man again—inside or outside the hospital ER. But his threat remained on my mind for months to come.

This was my first encounter with violence in the ED, directed at those caring for patients. Unfortunately, it was not the last.

Possessed

It was two o'clock on a Tuesday afternoon. Thus far, it had been a steady but not overwhelming day. My ER physician colleague and I both had a chance to eat something for lunch—an uncommon occurrence in the emergency department. Jeff had been brave enough to bring his lunch and stash it in the refrigerator, where poaching was a common practice. I, on the other hand, enjoyed the crisp texture and tasty flavor of peanut butter crackers.

Soon thereafter, I cared for a young man with a known seizure disorder who had just suffered a grand mal seizure before coming to the ER. Thankfully, he had been with his brother, who caught him before he fell to the ground at the onset of the seizure. That quick action prevented his brother from striking his face against a tile floor, which likely would have resulted in one or more facial lacerations.

As I stepped out of the room with the seizure patient, I heard a loud commotion down the hallway. At the far end of the corridor, I saw a woman come around the corner with a nurse on each side of her. She appeared to be in her midthirties, wearing jeans and a bright-red shirt. The nurses were trying to physically support the woman as they helped her make her way to a nearby patient room.

As I watched, the woman exhibited a strange behavior I had never seen before. She would take a step or two and then suddenly start screaming and yelling as she shifted her body position one way and then another. Sometimes she would flex forward as if she were going to touch her toes with her nose. Other times she would twist one direction and then the other as she flexed and unflexed her torso at the waist.

She was in constant motion, intermittently screaming and then mumbling softly, frequently putting her hands to the sides of her head. It was as if she were doing some sort of very strange and violently animated dance.

From a distance, it was hard to surmise what she might be suffering from. High on the list of potential diagnoses for patients with this type of unusual presentation are drugs (including alcohol) and psychiatric illness. Both of those conditions could result in a variety of unusual and sometimes extreme presentations.

As the woman and accompanying nurses got closer to the room to which they were heading, I looked at Cathy, the nurse on the patient's right, raising my eyebrows and slightly tilting my head in a nonverbal inquiry as to what the patient's problem was. As they turned the corner toward the room, still holding on to the twitching and jerking woman, Cathy mouthed to me in an exaggerated fashion, "She's possessed."

Yikes! I thought. While I had witnessed that condition in movies and on TV, I had not yet encountered it in the emergency room. With some degree of trepidation, I followed Cathy, Suzy and the patient into the room.

The nurses helped Mrs. Brown into the large chair in the room. It was the type of chair that was mounted on a swivel and could be positioned in many different ways, including all the way back until it was flat. It was very similar to what one might see at the dentist's office. The other rooms in the ER, which had stretchers, were all filled with patients, so this was the only available option.

Mrs. Brown sat in the chair momentarily, after which she leaped out of it and began jerking and flexing at her waist, lightly stomping her feet on the floor as she began turning in a circle. It almost looked like some sort of war dance a person might do around the campfire at night, especially if they had too much to drink. It was hard to make out exactly what she was saying as her pitch and cadence continually changed. I could only pick up bits and pieces.

"Oh, no! No! No! No!" she shouted when she was flexed forward, her face looking down at the ground with her hands at the side of her head, her feet shuffling forward as she moved in a circular pattern.

"Let me go! Don't do this to me! Leave me alone! Leave me alone!" she almost screamed as she danced. Then suddenly she stopped, straightened up, and looked at each one of us as if she were trying to discern whether we were friend or foe.

That look caused me to be on guard for any sign of aggression, readying myself to intervene if needed. It was a scary situation, not knowing what was going on in this woman's mind.

I slowly and carefully stepped toward her in a nonthreatening manner as she stood next to the chair, fairly motionless at that moment. I tried to gain her attention and direct her focus toward me.

"Mrs. Brown, I'm Dr. Grant. Can you tell me what seems to be the problem?" I hoped I could get the question across to her and receive some sort of verbal response before the next wave of activity manifested itself.

She looked in my direction, and despite her previous wild antics, I didn't discern an appearance or expression suggesting psychosis or illicit drugs. Of course, that was just a quick gut feeling.

"Get him out!" she whispered to me in a pleading fashion. "Please, get him out!"

OK, I thought, *maybe my gut feeling is off a little today.*

I entertained the likelihood she really did believe she was possessed by another being. Or perhaps she was hearing voices associated with a mental illness like schizophrenia. Another consideration was temporal lobe epilepsy, which could generate a wide spectrum of auditory hallucinations. I had to try to engage Mrs. Brown in order to narrow down the possibilities.

"Get who out of where?" I asked, having no idea where this would lead. My mind had started processing next steps if Mrs. Brown got out of control. We could begin with restraints so that we could medicate her as needed. But I first wanted to see if I could get more information from her.

"I don't know!" she exclaimed. "He's poking and buzzing inside my head!" As soon as the words left her mouth, she broke out into another dance with head bobbing, feet shuffling, moaning, and intermittent screaming.

Psychiatric illnesses can present in some of the strangest patterns imaginable. My mind momentarily flashed back to an incident a few months previous when the police brought in a woman on a stretcher. She was on all fours—her outstretched hands and knees on the stretcher with her back parallel to it.

I replayed the video in my mind. She was barking like a dog as they wheeled her through the open doors and down the hallway to a room. The police officers had picked her up at the bus station where she had been biting the tires of a bus and barking at the people trying to board the bus.

If Mrs. Brown were suffering from a psychiatric illness, I knew the psychiatrists would not wish to see her until she had been "medically cleared." That was certainly a reasonable perspective. Missing a medical cause for an altered mental state could have serious consequences. Yet trying to examine a wild, uncooperative patient was a substantial challenge.

As the nurses tried to get Mrs. Brown back into the chair, I stepped toward the door, where there was a light switch on the wall.

"Mrs. Brown," I said, "I'm going to darken the room a little bit to see if that helps." I had learned that decreasing the light intensity could have a calming effect on some people, making them less agitated due to the decreased visual stimuli. On the other hand, if the patient has some degree of paranoia, it could make them more anxious or upset.

I watched to see what response Mrs. Brown might have with my hand still on the switch, the door of the room ajar about a foot so that there was still some light entering the room.

I was happily surprised to see it provide a degree of comfort. The frequency and intensity of her outbursts seemed to lessen over the next several minutes.

I took that opportunity to hurriedly examine Mrs. Brown, starting with her head. I explained to her what I was going to do as I took the ophthalmoscope and checked the responsiveness of her pupils, which could tip me off to whether certain drugs were on board. Then I looked at the back of her eyes to see if there was any evidence of brain swelling, which could point to a mass effect in her brain. There was none.

I rapidly moved to her ears as I continued my search to identify any basis for her extraordinary behavior. There might be blood behind her eardrum, suggesting some sort of recent head trauma, or perhaps an insect in her ear canal causing pain or "buzzing," a term she had used when she wanted "it" to get out of her.

Her right ear canal was clear, and I quickly looked into her left canal. Peering through the magnified lens into the brightly lit ear canal, I was startled to see two dark elliptical eyes staring back at me with antennae above each eye, originating from a spot near the center of the critter's head. I could also see the yellowish color of its head, scored with black lines. And I noted additional yellow color on the body of the insect behind its ugly face. It almost completely filled the width and depth of Mrs. Brown's ear canal.

I hurriedly removed the light of the otoscope from her ear, thinking it might further irritate the insect. I knew that its movement against her eardrum and the intermittent buzzing of its wings created a deafening amount of noise that translated into intense pain for her.

The magnified image of the insect's hideous face with black oval eyes was emblazoned upon my mind. I instantly knew what it was—a yellow jacket, a stinging type of wasp! I was much more familiar with these devilish creatures than I wanted to be.

For a moment, I briefly felt nauseated and a little light-headed. As a child, I had been stung by them several times with one incident in particular that made me hate—and fear—them.

I was about eight years old playing in our backyard when a yellow jacket landed on my left arm near my elbow. I had been stung by one before and remembered the intense pain, so I immediately froze, incredibly afraid of what it might do. I dared not swat at it because I knew it would sting me. I naively wished it would just rest for a moment and then fly away.

Rather than depart, it looked at me with its repulsive face, inclusive of those black elliptical eyes. Then it began to very slowly crawl up my arm, which was extended out to my side. I watched it, those dark eyes intermittently looking toward my face and then back toward my shoulder as it unhurriedly made its way up my arm. Occasionally, it would pause. Each time it did, I hoped it had decided to fly away but was terrified it might have chosen to sting me instead.

I waited in fearful apprehension, anticipating the abrupt onset of that excruciating, burning, piercing pain I had experienced before, remembering how it had lasted for hours before it began to diminish even a little.

It was as if the evil creature wanted to torture my mind with that memory before it would then start to slowly move again.

I watched as it now approached the edge of my short-sleeved shirt. I knew if it got under my shirtsleeve, I would certainly be stung. I slowly and carefully extended my arm upward a bit further, intending to narrow the gap between the edge of the shirtsleeve and my skin.

Thankfully, the slow movement of my arm had worked. I hoped that when the yellow jacket encountered the fabric of my shirtsleeve it would dislike the tactile sensation of the material and fly away. Sweat was now dripping off my face—not because of the afternoon heat but rather from my racing heart and intense anxiety.

As it reached my shirtsleeve, it stopped to look toward my face again, as if it wanted me to guess what its next move was. It then crawled onto the cloth and continued upward toward my shoulder. Having reached that destination, it turned and began to creep toward my neck, each of its six legs moving slowly and rhythmically forward.

With it now approaching my neck, I didn't want to turn my face toward it for fear of being stung on my face, especially near my eyes. I could now barely see it out of the left corner of my eye.

I knew it was about to disappear from my vision. Fearful of where it might go after it left my line of sight, I could not contain myself any longer. I quickly reached up and tried to swat it off my shoulder with my right hand. As I did so, I suddenly felt the intense, piercing pain on my neck as it punctured my skin and injected its venom into my flesh.

I screamed and ran for the house. It felt as though someone had taken a hot poker from the fire and touched it to the skin of my neck. And as I ran, I feared another sting, not knowing whether it was still on me or flying close by, ready to attack again.

As painful as that sting was, later in life, I realized that the greater pain was the emotional suffering from the apprehension and fear I experienced while watching the yellow jacket slowly crawl up my arm toward my neck. That mental anguish had become deeply entrenched in my soul.

The sight of the yellow jacket in Mrs. Brown's ear canal, magnified greatly through the otoscope, flooded my mind with that deep loathing, hatred, and fear of the malevolent winged creature.

A few seconds had passed following my withdrawal of the light from Mrs. Brown's ear. I was surprised the light hadn't irritated the wasp further. In my experience, it didn't take much to incite the aggressive response of a yellow jacket.

I needed to inform Mrs. Brown of what I had seen. I moved close to her and whispered near her right ear, "Mrs. Brown, please be still and quiet. You have a bug in your left ear, and if you shout or move about you may cause it to stir." Her eyes got as big as dinner plates, affirming my choice to use the word "bug" rather than "wasp" or "yellow jacket."

"It is what's causing the buzzing and scratching sound in your head." I wanted to let her know she was not possessed or having a mental breakdown, and there was a specific cause for what she was experiencing, which we were about to address.

I hoped she wouldn't freak out with the info (I might have if it had been me). I needed her assistance in getting the yellow jacket out without making the circumstances worse. Although it, amazingly, hadn't yet stung her with all the screaming, dancing, hands over her ears, and other activities, repetition of those actions might push it past its stinging threshold.

Perhaps, however, the wasp felt safe in that confined spot and just ignored all of the external events. Or maybe the darkened room had a soothing influence on the insect. In any case, its decreased movement had also calmed Mrs. Brown.

Now the question was how best to get it out without causing it to sting her, just as it had done to me those many years ago. If the wasp stung the wall of her ear canal, the tissue would rapidly swell and could trap the yellow jacket inside her ear canal. That could be excruciatingly painful as it struggled to get free, potentially damaging her eardrum. And unlike honeybees, yellow jackets can sting more than once.

There were three approaches for removing insects from the ear canal I had read about but not yet employed. One was to use a flashlight in a darkened room. For some insects, they move toward the light, as evidenced by the bugs seen flying around an outdoor light bulb.

A second approach was to add a drop or two of water into the patient's ear canal, with the patient lying on their side. If the bug didn't like getting wet, it would exit the canal to find a better, drier place to hang out.

Lastly, it was thought that the drug lidocaine, a local anesthetic, could actually paralyze an insect so it couldn't move or struggle, thereby decreasing the amount of pain and injury it could cause the patient. Unfortunately, it wasn't clear how long it might take to paralyze different insects when dripping lidocaine into the ear canal. If the insect got mad before the lidocaine worked it could generate some significant pain.

I decided to go with option one first. It didn't really have a down side if it failed. We could always try another option subsequently. Of course, if it did work, we would have a hard time finding the yellow jacket in the darkened room. I didn't relish the thought that I would be holding the light to which the yellow jacket might be attracted. I didn't want it within a hundred yards of me!

I softly whispered to Mrs. Brown, informing her of what I was about to do, instructing her to try to hold very still if she felt it moving. Then I positioned her head so her left ear canal would be pointed in the direction of where I would stand.

I planned to use my penlight, which was very bright, holding it near Mrs. Brown's ear and then slowly moving it away from her. I had no idea what the right amount of brightness and distance would be for this to work.

I positioned Suzy, one of the nurses, at the door with her hand on the light switch. If the yellow jacket came out and took flight, I wanted to see where it was going. Cathy stood next to Mrs. Brown, on the opposite side of where I would be. She gently put her hands on Mrs. Brown's hands to encourage her to not reach up if she felt the insect moving.

I walked to the wall cabinet in the room, opened it, and took out a large towel. If the yellow jacket flew toward me, I wanted to be prepared for battle. A large folded towel was much better than a fly swatter. Of course, if I had access to a rocket launcher, I would have chosen that instead.

With everyone in position, I instructed Suzy to shut the door, making the room pitch black, except for a thin strip of light at the bottom of the door. I waited for a moment and then switched on my penlight about eighteen inches from Mrs. Brown's left ear. I waited a few moments and then very slowly began to back up. I had only taken a short step or two before I thought I saw movement at the edge of her ear canal. I stopped and held the spot.

I could see Mrs. Brown tightening up while also hearing her whimper softly. Cathy held her hands.

Then I saw the yellow jacket's head and upper body emerge from Mrs. Brown's ear canal. In that moment, I couldn't believe it was working! In another second, the yellow jacket had completely exited her canal and was on her outer ear, moving its wings as if it were about to take off.

Mrs. Brown had done the best she could do. At that point, she couldn't stand it anymore. In a flash, she pulled her right hand out from under Cathy's hands and tried to swat away the "bug" from her left ear where she had felt it moving.

Oh, no! I thought.

It disappeared from Mrs. Brown's ear and into the darkness. I was unable to tell which direction it was headed. With some degree of excitement and fear, I hurriedly shouted at Suzy to turn on the light, after which I scanned the room, searching for the malevolent creature.

Cathy, Suzy, and I all looked at Mrs. Brown first to be sure it hadn't returned to her. Mrs. Brown suddenly leaped from the chair and dashed for the door. Cathy apparently liked the idea and swiftly followed Mrs. Brown. Anticipating their plan, Suzy had opened the door for them and then also followed, *closing it* as she exited.

That left me alone in the room with the villainous nemesis from my past. I had tricked the depraved creature out of its safe haven, and I imagined it now wanted to settle the score. I could not help but hastily glance at my scrubs to be sure Mrs. Brown hadn't inadvertently brushed it onto me. It was controlled panic as I scoured every inch of my clothing.

Feeling somewhat assured it hadn't landed on me, I then scanned the room, towel in hand, ready to attack or defend.

Then I saw it. The stinging insect had landed on the stainless-steel Mayo stand—a tall metallic stand with two long, skinny rectangular feet on the bottom and a flat, slightly recessed tray on the top. The yellow jacket was on the edge of the tray closest to me, about four feet away and at waist height. It was watching me as it moved its wings back and forth, fully extending them and then bringing them back against its body, clearly getting ready for takeoff.

I knew if it became airborne, it would have the advantage. I needed to attack quickly. I slowly and cautiously raised the towel above my head as I carefully moved within striking distance. I could see its elliptical black eyes and short antennae. It cocked its head slightly as if it were daring me to try to swat it. I knew how aggressive they could be, and if I missed, it would be after me. Perhaps that was its plan—draw me in, wait for the right moment, and then attack.

It was as if two gunslingers were shifting their position as they squared off on the main street of a dusty town in the Old West, waiting to see who would make the first move.

I did!

With towel in hand, I swatted at the hideous insect as fast and as hard as I could, knocking the metal Mayo stand off its feet, the tray flying against the tiled wall and the remainder of the stand clanging down onto the floor. The noise was deafening as the sound bounced around the reflective surfaces of the closed room.

Almost in a panic, I searched for the yellow jacket, knowing that if I hadn't killed it, the loathsome pest would be sure to attack me, probably from my blind side. I rapidly swiveled my head from side to side, trying to locate it with my visual radar.

Then I saw it. The yellow-and-black insect was on the floor only a few feet in front of me. It was standing on its six legs, wings spread out and, once again, about to take off. I supposed the wind from the towel had knocked it to the floor without really injuring it. Now it was about to take flight and return fire. It was looking right at me. I could see vengeance in its eyes.

Quickly, I acted, vaulting forward, right leg extended, trying to get my tennis shoe above it before it lifted off. Just as my shoe was about to pass over it, I saw it take off, coming in my direction. For a brief moment, I panicked, imagining that it might fly out from underneath my shoe before the shoe touched the floor. If successful, it might fly right up the leg of my scrub bottom and deliver its payload of venom into my skin. Past fears flooded my mind.

But I soon recognized it had miscalculated. I could see its head with beady eyes just beyond the heel edge of my shoe, its body most likely flattened under my footwear. If it had chosen to fly in a direction other than right at me, I would have missed, leaving myself exposed to its air attack, completely off-balance with my legs spread apart. Instead, its heinous plan resulted in its ultimate demise.

I stood immobile for a few moments, basking in the success of my lightning-fast attack. I smiled, recognizing my actions had thwarted its wicked attempt to counterattack. I had avenged the emotional torment and painful sting its ancestors had delivered to me in my youth. Score settled. Complete and utter triumph!

Exiting the room and announcing absolute victory, I was able to entice Mrs. Brown back into the room to recheck her ear canal and eardrum—but only after she was able to see for herself the lifeless body of the reprehensible insect on the floor.

Her ear canal and eardrum were both undamaged. Now able to talk with her about how this had all unfolded, she told me she had been outdoors when she first felt that something had struck her ear. That was soon followed by the buzzing and scratching noise. She had no idea what had happened, just that the noise was painfully loud and seemed as if it were coming from inside her head. She was now able to go home, greatly relieved that her ordeal was over.

After her departure, the nurses teased me relentlessly for all the noise that came from the room after they had exited and the subsequent battle ensued. They envisioned me throwing everything in the room at the yellow jacket as it repeatedly dive-bombed me while also knocking over anything still standing as I tried to escape its attack. They razzed me for being afraid of a little insect, to which I reminded them of their rapid and frantic departure, smiling broadly.

Eventually, I told them of my yellow jacket encounters as a youth and then confessed my great pleasure in exorcising that demon from my past.

They smiled and then expressed their collective gratitude that it was the only exorcism needed that day.

Broken Heart

The heavy wooden doors catapulted open as a stretcher came barreling through. Carol, who had been the triage nurse out front, was right behind it, struggling as she guided the bed through the doors in what seemed like a reckless fashion. As she tried to make a quick left turn with the stretcher, she almost tipped it over, along with the patient it held. Clearly, she was trying to get to a major trauma room as quickly as possible.

The patient lying on the stretcher appeared to be a young female, probably in her late teens or early twenties. She was flailing her arms about and kicking her feet into the air. Intermittently, she was also screaming at the top of her lungs. From my vantage point at the other end of the hallway, it looked as though she were fighting off some imaginary demon that hovered above her.

At first, I thought Carol was bringing this young lady back to keep the patients in the waiting room safe from alarm, or possible harm. But why was she in this much of a hurry?

Carol completed her left turn with the stretcher and was now coming down the major hallway in which I had been walking after having seen another patient.

Suddenly, I saw the answer to my question. The young girl's white blouse was bloody on the left side of her chest.

With my speed now matching Carol's, we arrived simultaneously at Room 4, one of the major trauma rooms.

"Stab wound to the left chest," she said as we entered the room together. Two more nurses and two residents swiftly followed.

"Two lines, please," I said to the team as Carol locked the wheels of the stretcher as it came to rest in the center of the room. "Let's type and cross her for two units of blood to start with, and please get out a chest tube tray and CVP tray in case we need them."

The orders were just to ensure we were all on the same page. The nurses already knew that two large IV catheters were necessary in case the patient was rapidly losing blood internally from the chest wound. The two trays were packages containing a number of sterile instruments and materials needed for certain types of emergency procedures. It was always good to have them immediately available if required.

Any patient with a "penetrating" chest wound must be considered critically ill until *proven* otherwise. Even if the wound is small and there is little or no bleeding, and the patient appears normal, the physician *must* have the mindset that there could be a life-threatening injury to major blood vessels, one or both lungs, or even to the heart. A knife with a long, skinny blade could do terrible damage to internal organs while leaving a very small wound visible on the outside.

For that reason, it is imperative to rule out critical injuries as soon as possible. If the patient does have a serious internal injury, they could suddenly decompensate and potentially die in a span of just minutes—or even seconds.

To address the possibility of these grave concerns, a host of planned and orchestrated activities must happen quickly, beginning with a rapid exam, IV catheter insertions, and a blood draw for a complete blood count, toxicology, and chemistry tests in case the patient needs to have emergency surgery.

Additionally, the patient must be placed on oxygen along with monitors to track their heart rhythm and oxygen concentration in the blood. A 12-lead EKG is necessary to search for evidence of gross damage to the heart itself. X-rays then follow.

As the whirlwind of activities was about to commence, I wanted to reassure our patient, recognizing that the young girl must be terrified and traumatized by what had happened to her before getting to the ER. Now she would be feeling more pain and lack of control as the many actions and procedures happened around her, and to her.

My stethoscope was already in my ears, about to listen to both sides of her chest and her heart, to see if I could audibly detect any internal injuries. But I first spoke to her as I leaned over her right shoulder while she lay on the stretcher, visually assessing the injury to her left chest.

"Ma'am, my name is Dr. Grant. I know this must be very scary for you, but we want to help you. Can you tell me what happened?" I asked as I unbuttoned her shirt. She had no bra on, which made it easy to see a small half-inch laceration at the lower edge of her left breast. It was oozing a small amount of blood, but there was no bubbling from the wound, which was a good sign.

At this point, the young woman lay motionless on the stretcher, staring straight ahead with her eyes open. She had abruptly stopped screaming, kicking, and flailing her arms as she had come into the room. She did not answer my question.

As I waited for a response, I hurriedly listened for breath sounds on both sides of her chest, trying to determine if either of her lungs had been significantly collapsed from the injury. They were equal—another good sign.

Before I got my stethoscope out of my ears, one of the nurses called out vital signs.

"BP eighty-six, pulse one twenty and faint, respirations twenty-four," she said as she moved on swiftly to perform the next task.

"Miss, we're going to be doing a lot of things rapidly here to try to determine whether you have any serious injuries, so please don't be afraid. We're all doing the best we can to help you." I watched her face to see if there was a response.

Her blood pressure was low, but at her age, it was high enough for her brain to be perfusing, allowing her to think appropriately. As I waited again for a response, the coordinated activity around her continued. I glanced at her face, head, neck, and other parts of her body for visible evidence of other injuries.

"Can you tell me your name?" I asked as I leaned over closer to her face, hoping to distract her from all the other things going on. An appropriate response would allow me to momentarily assume she did not receive a serious head injury during the altercation. An inappropriate response would give me another high priority for evaluation.

As I gently put my hand on her abdomen to check for any tenderness, I once again asked if she could tell me what happened. The response was not what I anticipated.

The young patient suddenly screamed and started thrashing and kicking. Those working all around her performing various tasks had to hastily step back to avoid being struck. One of the IVs came out because it had not yet been taped down. Then the patient abruptly stopped after about five seconds and became quiet again—motionless, staring straight ahead. Everyone hurriedly resumed their assignments, recognizing how critically ill this patient could be under the circumstances.

"Her name is Patricia, Dr. Grant. Her driver's license says she is eighteen." The security person was in the room going through Patricia's purse looking for some sort of identification and medical information, like medications or allergies. "There is a ticket stub to a dance club."

I leaned over the edge of the stretcher so I could look directly at our patient. "Patricia, you're gonna have to help us so that we can help you." Again, she lay motionless with her blank stare straight ahead. "Patricia, I need you to talk to me, OK?" No response.

I continued my exam. Without Patricia's cooperation, I didn't know if there were other injuries or if she had only been stabbed once in the left side of the chest. I also did not know if she had any known medical conditions, allergies, or medications—or if she had any drugs or alcohol on board—all of which could impact her subsequent care.

I found no other evidence of trauma. They had restarted the IV that had been lost earlier and were in the process of taping it down when Patricia again started screaming, shaking her head from side to side and flailing her arms. Thankfully, at this point, they had put leather restraints on both her legs since one of the providers had nearly been kicked in the face earlier.

I had returned to the right side of the stretcher in an attempt to talk with her again when she started her combative behavior. She suddenly reached up with her right hand and grabbed my scrub shirt, trying to jerk me about. She had a powerful grip for a young lady of her age, but she wasn't able to yank me off-balance. I grasped her wrist and pulled her hand loose from my shirt, leaving a handprint of blood on the front of my scrub shirt.

The nurse had obtained her blood pressure and other vital signs before this latest outburst and now called them out to me: "Ninety over seventy, with a pulse of one thirty."

While Patricia's heart rate could be elevated due to her intermittently agitated state, it could also be from internal bleeding. Cardiac tamponade was yet another potentially fatal cause, a condition in which the sack around the heart fills with blood from an injury to the heart, progressively impeding the heart's ability to pump blood to the rest of the body.

A technician was now entering the room with portable equipment to take a chest X-ray, looking for evidence of a collapsed lung or significant bleeding into Patricia's chest cavity. The pressing urgency to rapidly identify the nature and extent of her injuries continued.

My initial approach with Patricia had been to maintain an even tone of voice and attempt to be reassuring. But at this point, I needed Patricia's immediate cooperation or we would lose precious moments in arriving at the correct diagnosis and initiating the appropriate therapy. I worried most about a wound to her heart or to a major blood vessel in her chest, which could kill her quickly if she didn't get definitive treatment in the operating room.

I had to try a different method to get through to Patricia. Her life was potentially in the balance, and losing time could mean losing her life.

After I pulled her hand away from my scrub shirt, I held on to it and leaned over the stretcher close to her face. She abruptly jerked her head away from me. I reached with my other hand and turned her face back toward me, which she attempted to resist.

I looked her straight in the eyes and spoke firmly and deliberately to her, about ten inches from her face. "Do you want to live?" I'm certain that frustration and concern were both evident in my voice and on my face. No response.

I asked her again. "I said, 'Do you want to live?'" This time, I spoke louder. She tried to turn her face away, but I wouldn't let her. I continued to look directly into her eyes. Beads of perspiration were present all over the smooth skin of her face. I could see fright in her eyes. No response.

"*Do you?*" I emphatically asked one last time.

After hesitating for just a second, she nodded her head yes. She reached up and gently put her left hand over my wrist. "Please, I want to live. Please help me." I could see tears start to form in her eyes.

I now spoke softly without breaking eye contact. "Patricia, if you want to live, you're gonna have to help us." She was now listening as she looked at me.

"We need to figure out if you have injuries on the inside. We need you to hold still while we do a lot of things very fast and not fight against us. Some things are not going to feel very good, but you have to help us, OK?" I spoke gently, trying to be more reassuring.

She nodded again as tears streamed down both sides of her face. I could feel emotion starting to well up inside of me. For a split second, I felt a mix of great sorrow and anger over Patricia's situation—a teenage girl who had suffered a violent, potentially lethal injury through the senseless act of some deranged person at a party that got out of control. No matter what had been said or done, she did not deserve this. In that instant, I anguished over what she must be feeling and how frightened she must be—alone, and not knowing what might happen to her.

My mind reflexively pushed the emotion aside, refocusing on the importance of rapid diagnosis and treatment, which could potentially save her life.

From that point forward, Patricia was the perfect patient. She held absolutely still, even for some of the more painful procedures that had to be done—procedures that would give us the information necessary to make an accurate diagnosis. She didn't ask questions, she didn't complain, she didn't speak. She was completely cooperative.

We now moved faster, efficiently covering the ground needed to get definitive data. Everyone was giving Patricia positive reinforcement and trying to be supportive and encouraging during and after each procedure or test that was done, telling her what a great job she was doing. The wonderfully empathetic nurses intentionally made consistent eye contact with her, offering kind reassurance.

The information subsequently gained revealed an injury to her lung, but it was minor at the moment. The more serious finding was the stab wound had indeed injured her heart and blood was collecting in the sac around the heart, beginning to impair its ability to provide adequate blood flow to the rest of her body. It was a life-threatening injury that required emergency surgery in the operating room right away. The surgical team had already been notified and was in the ER about to take Patricia upstairs to the OR.

Everything necessary to prepare her for surgery had been done while the surgical team was on its way to the ER. With Patricia's cooperation, we had been able to rapidly arrive at a diagnosis while maintaining her blood pressure and other vital signs. She was going to enter surgery in a tenuously stable but very critical condition.

As they were unlocking the brakes on the wheels of her stretcher, I moved to her right side and leaned over and spoke to her reassuringly, knowing that things had been hectic and harsh for her earlier.

"Patricia, they're going to take you to surgery now so they can fix things up for you." She didn't move. She just continued to hold very still and once again stared straight ahead. I interpreted that as a new fear she was facing—she had never had surgery before and didn't know what to think. "They will take very good care of you."

As the stretcher moved toward the doorway, Patricia suddenly reached up with her right hand and grabbed my scrub shirt again. She pulled me down toward her, making me lean over the side rail of the stretcher as she tried to lift herself up, as far as the wire leads, IVs, and tubes connected to her would allow.

Our faces were about two feet apart, and I could feel her looking deep into my soul with her dark, sad eyes. I returned her gaze, and behind the fine beads of perspiration on her face, I could see the fear and apprehension that enveloped her. Empathy for her consumed me. I knew she must have felt all alone.

"Tell me I'm not gonna die," she pleaded, almost in a subdued cry. Her words clearly embodied the anxiety and loneliness that were so evident in her eyes. As she spoke, she tightened her grip on my shirt, drawing me a little closer. I couldn't break my eyes away from hers.

In the second it took for my response, I thought I should be completely honest and tell her we would do the best we could and her chances were very good. But before the words came out of my mouth, my mind flashed back to when she had first come in the door—flailing, wild, frantic, alone, and afraid.

"Tell me I'm not gonna die," she repeated. I knew that if she became hysterical now and started to thrash about, she would almost certainly dislodge some of her tubes and IV lines—losing time, which would almost certainly lead to her death from her very serious injury.

In that moment, the despair in her eyes seemed to be deepening.

"You're gonna make it," I said in a soft voice as I reached out with my left hand and gently touched her right cheek, where a tear had begun to trickle down. I brushed it away with my thumb and smiled at her.

"You help these people as much as you helped us, and you're gonna make it. You can count on it." I saw relief in her eyes as she loosened her grip and lay back on the stretcher. A tiny smile broke across her face. I continued to walk alongside the stretcher as it left the room, now with my left hand gently holding on to her right forearm, trying to provide her with some degree of comfort and reassurance as we approached the elevators that would take her up to the operating room.

I couldn't help but feel good. We had aided a frightened, combative young girl who'd suffered a life-threatening stab wound to her heart. In a very short time frame, we had established a definitive diagnosis to be addressed with immediate surgery. It was not an easy task under the best of conditions. With Patricia's assistance and composure, she now had a good chance of survival.

In the crowded elevator, Patricia lay on the stretcher facing me, surrounded by IV poles, monitors, and other equipment, along with the surgical team. I stood outside the elevator and smiled at her as the doors began to close, telling her I would check on her after surgery.

I headed back down the hallway of the ER to begin seeing other patients who had come in that busy evening. After several hours, we were caught up, having seen all the patients who had been waiting. With the ensuing lull, and other ER docs on shift, I headed upstairs to the operating rooms to see how Patricia's surgery was progressing.

As I rode the elevator upward, I hoped the surgical team would be finished and Patricia would be in recovery. Of course, I knew that was an unlikely possibility. Operating on a patient's heart was an amazingly difficult, complex, and perilous undertaking that required substantial time and effort, along with exceptionally talented surgeons.

Once off the elevator, I navigated through several sets of double doors to the hallway leading to the operating rooms. On the wall to my left was a very large whiteboard with multiple rows of information containing patient names, ages, sex, surgical problem, surgeon, anesthesiologist, and additional details.

I searched for Patricia's name and corresponding age and sex in case there was more than one patient with that name. As I scanned the board, I came up empty. While I was surprised, I was also encouraged, concluding that the surgery must have gone well and Patricia was now in the recovery room.

As I was about to head toward the surgical recovery area, a nurse came through the double doors that led to the operating rooms.

"Excuse me, I'm Dr. Grant from the ER. I was wondering if you are familiar with a teenager named Patricia who we sent up for surgery several hours ago. She had a stab wound to her heart, and I don't see her name on the board."

The young lady responded with a slight smile before she spoke. "Yes, I know the patient." Her statement was followed by a pause, causing me to instantly brace for unexpected news. "I'm very sorry to tell you that she did not make it through surgery."

Stunned by those words, I thought that perhaps we were talking about two different patients, so I began describing Patricia's appearance and her condition upon her arrival at the operating suite.

"Yes, I understand. Unfortunately, she did not survive the surgery. They were not able to save her."

I stood in the empty hallway, unable to fully accept the information the nurse provided me. I didn't *want* to accept it.

Then she spoke again. "I'm very sorry, but I need to attend to a patient." With those words, she hurriedly walked past me and down the corridor.

I remained standing in the hallway, wondering what could have gone wrong. My mind replayed the extraordinary team effort downstairs, in which the diagnosis of impending cardiac tamponade from her stab wound was rapidly made, and her condition in the ER quickly stabilized. That had given Patricia the chance to make it into surgery, where they could definitively address her serious injury.

Unfortunately, the course in the ER was only the initial portion of a very difficult journey. My mind forced me to accept that fact. Opening Patricia's chest to access and repair a wound to her beating heart, which supplied blood to her entire body, was an incredibly challenging endeavor. There were many potential difficulties that could hinder the desired outcome of her operation.

Still, I was numb, and I was heartbroken, as I knew her family and friends would be when they learned of the evening's events. I did not want to accept Patricia's death, as if that would somehow change the outcome.

I slowly walked over and sat down in one of the many empty chairs in the darkened surgical area outside the operating rooms. I thought about Patricia's ever-so-slight smile the last time I had seen her. I thought about how brave and cooperative she had been after the difficult start. I thought of the hope and assurance I had given her—which turned out to be baseless, and failed her. I once again became angry that someone had forced this injury upon her, and had senselessly taken her very young life. She seemed to have so much beautiful life and spirit in her.

I anguished over her loss. Tears flowed as I put my head in my hands and sat alone in the gloomy, unlit waiting area.

Later, when I drove home in the wee hours of the morning after my shift, the streets were dark with no traffic. Outside it was dreary and desolate, which reflected how I felt inside.

In the days and months that followed, I continued to mourn Patricia's loss.

Although she passed away that night, she has stayed with me. Now, more than twenty years later, I still see her face from time to time. And I still hear my answer to her question.

Each time, as I reflect upon that evening, tears form in my eyes and anguish weighs upon my soul. The weapon that pierced her heart and took her life injured mine as well.

The Later Years

Not Me

"So which dinosaur is your favorite?" I asked Jake, my patient lying on the stretcher next to me as I sat on the stool.

"That's hard!" Jake said as he closed one eye, grimaced a little, and looked up to the ceiling. Clearly, this question deserved serious thought.

Jake would have easily won the award for best patient of the day. He was only seven years old and in second grade but an incredibly happy and cooperative child.

When he had first come into the ER, I wasn't sure that would be the case. Jake had a one-and-one-half-inch, J-shaped laceration on the inner aspect of his left forearm. It had gone all the way through the skin and would clearly need stitches.

For many children, a cut that size, along with the bleeding, immediately triggers the thought of stitches. And stitches mean needles and shots and someone touching their wound—all of which can evoke terror in the mind of a child that age.

It's as if they have all heard various horror stories about stitches. Perhaps, it is a badge of courage that entices those who've had them to exaggerate the pain and suffering they may, or may not, have experienced—creating fear in the hearts of those who have not yet had stitches.

Early on in my career, I learned an incredible lesson from one of the wise nurses with whom I worked. She had an alternative approach to addressing the widely disseminated fear about stitches. At that time, I was in the room with her, along with a very anxious young boy who was worried about whether his cut would need stitches.

As Nurse Glenda took the child's vital signs and made some nursing notes, the weepy child asked if she thought the cut would need stitches. Wisely, Glenda looked at the cut again, made a wrinkled face as if she were thinking really hard about it, and said, "I think this cut will do just fine with some 'string Band-Aids' and *no* stitches!" Of course, she winked at me as she said it.

I was amazed at the immediate change in demeanor and cooperation of the child. Clearly, a tremendous burden had been lifted from his mind, for which he was exuberant! He was now looking forward to getting his magical string Band-Aids.

Of course, string Band-Aids and stitches were one and the same, differing only in name. The significant challenge would be getting them in without the child seeing the needle on the syringe for the local anesthetic, and the needle attached to the string portion of the string Band-Aids. That required a bit of skill, a variety of diversionary tactics, and a bit of a magic act.

But I knew it was doable. I remembered the dentist who cared for me when I was a young teenager. He filled many of my cavities over the years before I ever realized he was giving me a shot of local anesthetic inside my mouth prior to beginning the dental work.

He deftly hid the needle behind one of his hands as he had me tilt my head backward, further restricting my view. He did this for years until I was about eighteen. I suppose, at that age, he thought I could accept it without being fearful. The first time I became aware that I was about to receive an intraoral injection, however, my knuckles must have been as white as snow from me tightly gripping the chair.

Of course, every child is different. Jake was a cheerful, accommodating, intelligent child. He didn't have a high level of preconceived fear about the process, and he asked a lot of questions about how and what I would do to take care of his wound.

Recognizing it would be difficult to hide the needle throughout the procedure because of the wound's depth and shape, I explained that I would use some special "numbing" medicine that would make his cut go to sleep and, after that, he would not feel any pain. That would allow us to put in the string Band-Aids without any discomfort at all.

Avoiding the topic of needles, I explained how the medicine would feel cold to begin with and then feel warm, which meant it was working to make the cut go to sleep. I told him I needed someone to slowly count to thirty for me while the medicine was working.

Jake, of course, eagerly volunteered for the counting job. Out of his sight, I first drew up the lidocaine anesthetic in a syringe that had a needle on it. Then I removed the needle and turned toward Jake, showing him the syringe without the needle, explaining that I would use it like a tiny squirt gun to gently spray some of the magic medicine onto his cut so it would go to sleep. I then told him about our special paper with a hole in the center, which we would lay on his arm to keep germs away from his cut while we applied the string Band-Aids. He had to be very careful not to touch it.

Jake's eyes widened as I described the process, and he seemed ready to go on this new adventure. His cooperative attitude made me wish all the kiddos—and adults—with lacerations were like him.

At that point, I turned to Jake's dad, Mr. West, to excuse him from the room. He was a tall man in his late thirties with an athletic build, a black handlebar mustache, and a full head of curly black hair. He clearly lifted weights and had very muscular forearms and biceps, readily visible with his short-sleeve shirt. Some might have described him as having a macho appearance.

He had been quiet throughout my entire discussion with Jake.

"Mr. West, we're ready to get started, so if you'll head out to the waiting room, one of the nurses will come get you as soon as we're finished." I now had the sterile sheet of paper on Jake's arm with all of my sterile instruments on the tray next to me as I sat on the stool adjacent to the stretcher.

"Thanks, Doc, but I'll stay here while you work," was Mr. West's reply.

Oftentimes, children do better without their parents in the room, primarily because the parents can unintentionally give off signals of distress as they try to squeamishly watch what's being done, sometimes even adding sound effects like moans and gasps. The kiddos respond accordingly.

"Are you sure?" I asked. "We'll take very good care of him," I added, hoping the reassurance might encourage him to step out to the waiting room.

"Yep, I'm gonna stay," was his brief response.

"Alright, there's a chair next to the wall behind you. Please take a seat and we'll get started." If parents insist on staying, we always have them sit down. It's not uncommon for them to feel light-headed. If they are sitting, they have less distance to fall should they pass out.

"I'll just stand here and watch, Doc. But thanks anyway," Mr. West responded.

I had heard that response before, and I had seen the consequences. I tried to reason with Jake's dad.

"Mr. West, I really would like for you to sit down. I'm fine with you watching, but I don't want you to pass out and hit the floor. That's happened before to people who insist on standing, which is why we implore family members to sit down if they want to stay in the room."

I heard the snort before he spoke. "Doc, I was a medic in Vietnam. I've seen more blood than you can imagine. A little cut on the arm doesn't even register for me."

I turned around on my stool to look his way. He stood about three feet behind me, tall and straight with his arms folded across his chest. He gave me what I interpreted to be his tower-of-strength look. I was unfazed.

I spoke in an even tone of voice. "I'm sure you must have seen a lot of trauma, but this is different. This is *your* child. Trust me—it's different when you're watching someone treat your family member." I paused, hoping he would listen to a voice with experience in this setting. "Please do me a big favor and take a seat."

I wasn't sure whether he was trying to impress his son or just wanting to exude toughness.

"I'm good, Doc. Really, I'm fine," was his response as he maintained his body posture.

"If you won't sit down now, then please do so in a hurry if you start to feel light-headed or woozy or sick to your stomach. You're a tall man, and it's a long way to the floor." I spun back around to Jake, who had remained quiet during my brief discussion with his dad.

I heard the snort again. "Will do, Doc, will do."

I now focused entirely on Jake. We had gotten off to an incredibly good start, and I wanted to stay on that path. It's good to engage children of his age in conversation to keep their minds on things they're interested in so they are less likely to be anxious about the possibility something might hurt.

After I had dripped some lidocaine onto the open wound, Jake noted that it was indeed cold but didn't hurt. I let it sit for twenty to thirty seconds as I began to ask him about movies, sports, and other things children his age might have an interest in.

Then we came to stage two.

"OK, Jake, now for the special part I need your help with. I'm going to squirt some more medicine into your cut, and this time, it's going to feel warm and tingly, which means it's going to sleep. I need you to slowly count to thirty by saying 'one Mississippi, two Mississippi,' and so on, all the way up to 'thirty Mississippi.' Keep your eyes closed and think about every number when you say it. When you get to thirty, open your eyes, and we'll see how asleep your cut is. Can you do that?"

Of course, Jake was all in. He gleefully agreed and waited for my signal to start counting. I had the syringe with lidocaine in my hand ready to go.

"OK, start," I said. As soon as Jake closed his eyes and started counting, I picked up the needle for the syringe, attached it, and began to gently and slowly inject the lidocaine into the open wound.

There is a common misconception that if the needle is inserted into an open wound, it will really hurt. I can remember thinking that myself as a child. Actually, the opposite is true. Most of the pain fibers that detect the sharp, stabbing sensation are in the skin itself.

With the gap in the skin created by the injury, it's easy to bypass the skin and painlessly introduce the needle into the subcutaneous tissue below the skin. Jake didn't know the needle had actually entered his wound because his eyes were closed.

If one slowly injects the lidocaine, it generates a warm feeling as the medicine goes into the tissue. If injected too rapidly, it will actually produce a burning sensation, which is uncomfortable. I've had enough of my own wounds sewn up to have gained a wealth of experience regarding the nuances of local anesthesia and wound repair.

By the time Jake got to thirty, I had finished injecting enough lidocaine to numb the wound, and I removed the needle from the syringe.

"Open your eyes, partner!" I said as he hit thirty. "Fantastic job! You are a great counter!" Jake's face was beaming.

"Did you feel it getting warm and tingly?" I asked, reinforcing that everything we had talked about was what had taken place—with no surprises.

"Yes, it got warm but then it started to go away."

"So it was cold first, and in the next part, it got warm?" I asked.

"Yep," was Jake's response, still smiling.

"So, is your cut supposed to be asleep now?" I asked, hoping we were on a roll.

"Yep," he said, staying right with me.

"Alright, then, let's test it. Are you OK with me touching it to show you it is asleep? I can promise you that it is indeed sleeping. You will feel a little bit of pressure, but it will not hurt at all. It will feel like this," I said as I used my index finger to gently push against the side of his upper arm.

Jake's exuberance had decreased a little, but he was still on board. He nodded in a positive fashion in answer to my question.

After putting on my sterile gloves, with my index finger, I gently touched his wound and asked him, "Does that hurt?"

Somewhat amazed, he smiled, and said, "I can't feel anything!"

I touched it a couple of other places and pushed on it, demonstrating that it was indeed "asleep" and he wouldn't feel any pain. Jake thought it was really cool. It was something he couldn't have imagined.

I then took the next step and told him I was going to use a magic needle on the end of the string Band-Aids, and he would not be able to feel anything as the string passed through his skin. Based on our conversation and Jake's cooperation thus far, I didn't anticipate any issues.

After the first stitch was in, Jake was a firm believer. Again, he thought it was so cool that it didn't hurt and that he really couldn't feel much of anything.

With potential anxieties now alleviated, we dove into the discussion of dinosaurs. Thankfully, as a child, I had loved dinosaurs as well and developed a reasonable knowledge of the subject that allowed me to communicate intelligently with Jake.

"I would have to say the stegosaurus," was Jake's answer to my question about a favorite dinosaur. "He's really unusual, with all those plates on his back to protect him and that tail with spikes on it." I could tell, however, that he hadn't truly locked in on that answer.

As I put another suture through Jake's skin on his forearm and gently drew the edges of the skin together and tied the knot, he spoke again.

"Of course, the ankylosaurus is really cool too. He has all that armor with spikes on his back and a big club at the end of his tail." He smiled at me as he related his newest thought. "He could probably break a bone if he hit another dinosaur with that tail."

Clearly, Jake was mentally immersed in the world of dinosaurs as he looked again to the ceiling, no doubt thinking of another dinosaur that might unseat those he had already mentioned as his favorites.

As I put the next suture in, I drew together a broader gap in the wound, which caused some of the blood to ooze out along the wound's edges. I reached for a gauze square to sponge away the blood so I could see the skin edges better, after which I put it back on the tray next to me and then began tying the knot.

Suddenly, there was a loud crash behind me and to my right. I immediately turned to see tall Mr. West slumped in a semi-sitting position against the wall adjacent to the metal crash cart that was now slightly ajar. As he lay crumpled in this corner, his eyes were closed as he was actively seizing, his total body twitching with his head bobbing.

Oddly, Jake had not reacted strongly to the noise. To some degree, he was shielded from the sound as well as the view. The head end of the stretcher he lay upon was raised about forty-five degrees, and the stretcher was pointed in the direction opposite of where his dad had fallen. Jake had turned his head to the left where I was seated, but his dad was out of his field of vision.

Not wanting to call his attention to what had happened, I promptly said, "Jake, you think about that favorite dinosaur while I get me another pair of gloves. Can you hold real still and not move while I do that?"

Jake smiled at me, nodded yes, and then went back to contemplating his world of dinosaurs.

I hurriedly rolled my stool away from the stretcher before getting off to kneel down and support Mr. West's neck and head. I needed to move him away from the wall so I could lay him flat on the floor. He was seizing because his heart rate and blood pressure were low from what is known as a "vagal response," which can happen when people see things that make them sick to their stomach.

With my right leg, I pushed the heavy crash cart away from Mr. West while still supporting his head and neck. With the extra space I had created, I was now able to lay Mr. West flat onto the floor. As I did so, I noticed the blood on the wall and on my gloves. He must have hit his head first on the wall or the metal crash cart on his way down. He was going to have a whopper of a headache. Hopefully, he had not cracked his skull.

After laying him flat, his seizure abruptly abated. I checked his pulse rate, which was slow but increasing. At that point, one of the nurses came in, having heard the noise. With her arrival, I grabbed another pair of sterile gloves off the counter next to me and got back on my stool and rolled over next to Jake.

I turned back toward Helen, the ER nurse now kneeling at Mr. West's side. "My current patient is unaware of our new patient you're now attending to." Helen readily understood. If Jake knew his dad had just passed out and cracked his head, he might want to get up before we were finished.

"Our new patient had an episode of vasovagal syncope and fell. Can you slip a cervical collar on him and get some vital signs?" I asked Helen from Jake's bedside. She answered in the affirmative and went to work.

"Sir, please stay flat," Helen told Mr. West as he began to come around, his heart rate and blood pressure now adequate enough to perfuse his brain. Helen had already grabbed a hard plastic cervical collar from one of the cabinets and was slipping it onto Mr. West as he lay on the floor.

"Sir, you passed out and fell. The doctor wants you to stay flat on the floor until he can check you over. Please hold still and do not try to get up."

Helen, like most of the ER nurses, had seen this scenario before. Some patients who pass out try to quickly get back up because they are embarrassed about falling or because they are a little confused after their head injury. If their heart rate and/or blood pressure is still low, then as soon as they get up, they are unable to adequately pump blood upward to their brain and so they pass out and fall a second time.

Thankfully, Mr. West followed instructions *this* time.

While Helen attended to Mr. West, I was able to wrap up my conversation with Jake and finish stitching his wound closed.

"Jake, you have been my best patient of the entire day! Actually, the best patient of the whole week! I wish I could keep you around to tell other patients what to expect, and to help me when I'm putting in string Band-Aids."

Jake smiled and nodded as if he were ready for the job.

"Guess what?" I said to him as I took off my gloves. "You can actually help me with my next patient. You already know him."

Jake's smile turned to a quizzical look.

"While I was working on you, your dad had a dizzy spell and bumped his head." I gave that a few seconds to sink in, knowing it might be a bit confusing. "He's lying on the floor right behind us. He seems to be OK, but we're going to get some X-ray pictures to check things out. Then you can help me when I put some string Band-Aids on his cut."

I spoke loudly enough so both Jake and his dad could hear the plan. I was concerned that Jake might be upset, but when he looked around the edge of the stretcher toward his dad, Mr. West lifted his right hand as he lay on the floor and waved at Jake, who actually responded with a smile. He was certainly a contented child!

I then switched places with Helen, who put a bandage on Jake's arm as I checked Mr. West's neurological status and performed a complete exam in search of other potential injuries. I found none other than his head (and perhaps his pride). When I asked what he remembered, he gave the classic response.

"I was just watching what you were doing, and all of a sudden, I started to feel sort of woozy and light-headed. The next thing I knew, I was on the floor." After a brief pause, he confessed, "I guess I should have listened to you."

"Well, we'll get you fixed up. I'm going to send you to X-ray to get some pictures of your skull and neck. You've got a nice-sized gash on the back of your head. It looks like you may have hit the wall or the side of the cart on your way down. I want to make sure there's no crack in your skull before I close the wound with some string Band-Aids."

I smiled and winked at Jake, who had now joined us at his dad's side.

"I've got my expert with me who can tell you what to expect when we get ready to put in the string Band-Aids." I paused as I looked over at Jake, who was grinning.

"I just hope you can be as good a patient as he was!"

~ ~ ~

Sometimes, as we go through life, adults may act like children. And, at times, our children may teach us how to act like adults. Certainly, it has been true in my life as a parent—my children have taught me many valuable and wonderful lessons, for which I will always be grateful.

A Mother's Love

I heard the curtain behind me snap back quickly as I sat on a stool talking with the patient in Room 11.

"Dr. Grant, we have a three-year-old near drowning en route—only a few minutes out!" Alana, one of the ER nurses on shift, disappeared as rapidly as she had delivered the message. I excused myself from my patient and hurried toward Major Resuscitation Room 3, where they had already begun making preparations for the arriving ambulance.

As I turned the corner of the hallway leading to Room 3, I saw bright flashing red lights outside through the glass doors of the ambulance entrance at the end of the hallway. Paramedics were already unloading the stretcher with their patient on it.

I rushed into Room 3, glancing around to assess our state of readiness. Judy and Alana were our nurses, Gerald our respiratory therapist, and Amy our tech. Iris, the secretary, had already notified radiology that we would need a portable X-ray and asked the lab to send a tech to the ER. Knowing the competence of all the staff at the ready gave me great comfort and assurance.

I turned toward the doorway as I heard the paramedics approaching. I glanced at the stretcher to see a child lying motionless on the large EMS gurney, his eyes closed and his color pale. He seemed so small surrounded by three tall, broad-shouldered men in their fire department turnout gear frantically moving as rapidly as they could. It was a sight that would crush the heart of anyone, especially a parent.

The paramedics hurriedly swung the stretcher into the room. One of them was using a pediatric BVM (bag-valve-mask device) to assist the child's breathing, but they were not performing CPR, which was a relatively good sign. Drowning is a leading cause of death in children younger than five, and prolonged CPR without a pulse is a poor indicator for survival.

EMS and ER personnel swiftly transferred the three-year-old child from the ambulance gurney to the ER stretcher in the center of the room. They simultaneously transitioned specific equipment such as the oxygen tubing and cardiac monitoring. The EMS stretcher was then whisked out the door, giving us the needed space to all concurrently access the patient. During that brief period of time, the lead paramedic provided a concise report of what had transpired.

Ten minutes earlier, Mikey, the small boy on the stretcher, was found by his mother floating facedown in their pool. He had slipped out the glass door next to the patio and headed to the pool when his mother had briefly left his side to answer a phone call. When the mother recognized his absence, she frantically ran out to the pool, where she found him floating in the water. She jumped in and was pulling him out just as the paramedics arrived.

A friend with the mother had dialed 911 as soon as they saw the child in the pool. Luckily, there had been an ambulance passing close by on its way back to the fire station. It was able to respond and arrive at the scene within only a minute or two.

The initial assessment by the paramedics at the house revealed a bluish-colored child with no breathing, no pulse, no movement, and no response to any stimulation. They quickly scooped up the child and began rescue breathing as they headed for the ambulance, knowing the ER was only about three minutes away. Once in the ambulance, the paramedics began bagging Mikey with 100 percent oxygen, attempting to breathe for the child while en route to the ER.

They also connected him to the cardiac monitor as they rushed to the hospital. It revealed a very, very slow heart rhythm—an infrequent squiggly green blip that crossed the display from left to right. That very slow blip represented Mikey's only discernible sign of life.

They began CPR since he had no pulse. Shortly thereafter, Mikey's heart rate began to gradually increase from the ventilations and chest compressions being provided. Just as they pulled into the ER entrance, Mikey developed a pulse, allowing them to stop CPR as they prepared to unload him.

His small body now lay on the stretcher in front of me. He remained motionless and unresponsive to the whirl of activity that enveloped him.

His color was very poor. Instead of the rosy pink usually present in a child this age, Mikey's skin was mottled and dusky. As I listened with my stethoscope, I could hear harsh, noisy lung sounds as the respiratory therapist continued using the pediatric BVM to push oxygen into the child's lungs. I felt for a femoral pulse, which was present but only occurring at about half the normal rate for a child of this age. Each beat correlated with the shapes crossing the cardiac monitor on the wall above the stretcher.

Mikey's eyes were now open but glazed over with no movement and no evidence of the fright one would expect to see on the face of an injured or sick child brought into a strange place with strange people. He had no response when one of the nurses placed a tourniquet on his arm to draw blood.

No doubt his mind had been stunned or injured from the hypoxia, or lack of oxygen, he had suffered while underwater and during the subsequent period of time when his breathing, heart rate, and blood flow were impaired.

In that first minute after his arrival, the room around me was a blur of motion as nurses obtained vital signs, assembled IVs, prepared intubation equipment, and accessed supplies to draw blood. I now focused my efforts on assessing Mikey's ability to respond.

"Mikey, can you hear me?" I asked somewhat loudly as I leaned over him, filling his line of sight. Surprisingly, his eyes twitched the tiniest bit toward me, which I interpreted as a positive response.

Perhaps from all the stimulation to him—removing the wet clothes, covering him with warm blankets, attaching a blood pressure cuff and monitoring devices, and poking him with a needle to draw blood—he abruptly produced a weak cough, which sounded extraordinarily wet. One could hear the fluid in his airways without a stethoscope.

In these early moments of Mikey's care, I had reached an important therapeutic crossroad—how best to handle Mikey's airway and breathing.

In the rapid initial assessment, it was clear Mikey had inhaled and swallowed a large amount of water, which is typical for most near-drowning cases. Also, his stomach had ballooned significantly as the pediatric BVM was used to force air into his lungs, simultaneously pushing air into his stomach, where it became trapped, distending his abdomen. As the stomach enlarges, it pushes upward against the diaphragm, which then compresses the lungs, making it more difficult for the patient to take breaths and fill their lungs with oxygen.

I would need to insert a tube through Mikey's mouth into his stomach to remove all the water and air so his diaphragm could lower, allowing his lungs to expand and better oxygenate. But that process could make him vomit. Some physicians feel that a patient in this setting, with an altered mental status like Mikey's, should first be intubated to protect their airway.

I had seen children of this age and in this condition sometimes respond to less invasive efforts, so I hurriedly tried another approach.

"Mikey, let's see if we can get some water out," I said as I slipped my hands into his armpits. I motioned to Gerald, our respiratory therapist, to take away the BVM. I intended to lift Mikey up and then lay him across my left forearm and left thigh with his head down as I sat on the stretcher. I then planned to thump him on his back a few times to try to stimulate a cough.

But Mikey must have read my mind. As soon as I lifted him off the stretcher, he let out a strong cough followed by a gag, this time bringing up a large amount of pool water. His aim was slightly off-center, though, as he primarily drenched my left shoulder and the left side of my chest.

I noticed his color improving almost immediately. I went ahead and laid him across my left forearm and thigh in the head-down position, gently but firmly clapping his back a few times. He again brought up more water, but not as much as the first episode. His color now began to regain the anticipated pink, and he started to cry loudly, intermittently belching some of the air and water that had been trapped in his stomach. His cry had become strong and clear, generating excitement for everyone in the room!

As I laid him back on the stretcher, Gerald raised the head of the bed slightly, putting Mikey at about a thirty-degree angle.

Recognizing that Mikey's alertness and respiratory efforts had substantially improved (and Mikey had entered a less cooperative state of mind), Gerald placed an oxygen mask on him rather than attempting to use the pediatric BVM.

Concurrent with his cry, Mikey's heart rate swiftly increased into the normal range for a child his age. Reassessing his vital signs revealed an elevated pulse rate, an elevated respiratory rate (due to crying), a normal blood pressure, and an oxygen saturation reading now in the normal range—all of which were wonderfully positive signs to have appeared so quickly!

And perhaps most encouraging was Mikey's alertness. His eyes now darted around the room, no doubt looking for his mother or some other comforting and reassuring presence. I briefly reassessed his neurologic status, noting that he was moving all four extremities equally well and his interaction was now appropriate for his age.

Of course, Judy and Alana did their best to comfort him, talking softly in their reassuring, motherly voices with big smiles on their faces. Having removed Mikey's wet clothes upon arrival, they added more warm blankets on and around his little body as they interacted with him.

Mikey's incredibly rapid transformation from critically ill to a much-improved and now stable status indicated his treatment for the near term would primarily be continued oxygenation, monitoring, and close observation. Because complications might occur during the next twenty-four to forty-eight hours, he would need to be admitted to the hospital.

The radiology technician was now moving equipment into the room to take a chest X-ray, which would provide additional information about Mikey's lungs and how they were responding to the insult of being underwater and without oxygen.

Iris brought Mikey's initial lab results into the room, having just received them from lab personnel who called them to us as soon as they were available. Thankfully, they were all normal—another positive sign.

Henry, one of the X-ray techs, soon brought in Mikey's chest X-ray and popped it up on the view box in the resuscitation room. It was only slightly abnormal in the lung fields, which was no immediate cause for concern with his oxygenation saturation continuing to remain in the normal range.

Having received the encouraging information on top of his rapid and amazing improvement in clinical status, my thoughts immediately went to his mother.

I could only imagine the grief and suffering she was experiencing under the circumstances. The last image she had of her three-year-old son was a blue, lifeless, unresponsive, and motionless child. I couldn't bear the thought of her continued agony, unaware of Mikey's quick and extraordinary recovery. The nurses would alert me if there was an unexpected change in Mikey's condition, so I headed to the waiting room.

There were only two or three people in the waiting area, and when I asked, no one answered as Mikey's mom. Instead, someone pointed to the registration desk. I hurriedly walked through the waiting room to the hallway that led to registration.

As I turned the corner, I saw a woman who I instantly knew was Mikey's mother. Her image will forever be burned into my mind. She was a short, blonde-haired woman in her late twenties or early thirties standing alone in front of the registration desk in a wet shirt and shorts trying to provide answers to the clerical person who was asking questions and entering her responses into the computer.

As Mikey's mom leaned on the counter between them, I could see her tears falling onto the surface below. Mom was trying to provide whatever information she could in the hope of helping with some aspect of her child's care, mentally and emotionally holding it together at a time when most of us would be incoherent. Certainly, I would have been.

That brief visual clip caused a tsunami of emotion to flood over me in an instant. All of the things I blocked out of my mind from the moment I first saw little Mikey so that I could focus entirely on his care now evoked the feelings any parent would have for a child in such a tragic situation—not knowing whether their child would live or die.

At the same time, I could feel his mother's obvious and powerful love for him mixed with anguish and grief over the uncertainty of her son's condition. I could feel the helplessness she was experiencing, and imagined her potential sense of guilt over the momentary lapse of attention. And yet she stood there fighting through all of that terrible emotional pain as she tried to dutifully provide whatever medical information she could.

Tears welled up in my eyes.

"Mom," I said in a wavering voice as I walked toward her. She stopped talking to the clerk and turned to face me, her hands still clasped together on the countertop as if she had subconsciously been praying the whole time.

She looked at me in a questioning fashion, without any words, conveying a mixture of fear and hopefulness about what I was about to say. Her eyes were filled with compassion, love, and what seemed like a strength of great depth. Rivers of mascara on her cheeks revealed where waterfalls of tears had been flowing.

"Mikey's doing fine," I said softly, as quickly as I could get the words out. "Let's go see him." My voice faltered as I spoke, and I felt a tear cross my right cheek, falling onto the scrub shirt that Mikey had already drenched with some water of his own.

I held out my hand to Mom, thinking she might need some steadying after hearing the wonderful news. She stepped past my outstretched arm and put both of her arms around me in a bear hug, adding her tears to my own, now all mixed with Mikey's pool water.

As we briskly walked back to Room 3, I related Mikey's astonishing turnaround, due in large part to the excellent decision-making and exceptional performance of the EMTs and paramedics. I also let her know that even though he was doing very well at the moment, he could become more ill, so we needed to continue monitoring him closely. He would be admitted to the hospital for at least the next twenty-four-hour period.

When I opened the door to Major Resuscitation Room 3, Mikey immediately saw his mom and reached out both arms to her as his small body lay on the big stretcher, an oxygen mask on his face and an IV in his little arm. Clearly, he instantaneously recognized her—another good neurological sign for his recovery. I glanced at the monitors to process the latest data, all of which was excellent.

Mom hurriedly stepped to the stretcher, carefully leaning over the bed rail to comfort him, trying to be cautious of all the tubes and lines attached to her little boy, and, of course, he was crying for her.

I lowered the bed rail between them and motioned for her to sit on the stretcher next to him, then helped Mikey to get into his mother's arms without disconnecting his IV or EKG leads.

As Mom held Mikey, gently swaying from side to side, she profusely thanked everyone present, especially the paramedics and EMTs. The waterfalls of tears returned, this time with contributions from most everyone in the room.

Having the opportunity to experience such a rapid and wonderful turnaround in a small child whose condition began so ominously, and reuniting mother and child, is a joy that cannot be transcended. It is also a source of strength that helps to sustain one through the valleys of despair that certainly would lie ahead in other ER shifts to come.

Mikey's stay in the hospital for the next forty-eight hours was uneventful. He had no complications from his near-death experience and went home with his family, who carried with them the indescribable joy of a second chance at life that was almost lost.

Faith

"Dr. Grant, I placed a gentleman in Room 2 with some pretty nasty burns. You may want to see him next—he must really be hurting." Linda dropped the chart into the "To Be Seen" queue of charts on the counter, placing it ahead of several others waiting to be seen.

Linda had stopped at the nurses' desk just long enough to tell me about the patient before she was off again. That's what I admired about her—she was efficient, hardworking, and compassionate. She was a wonderful nurse one could count on in any circumstance.

As I stood at the nurses' station, I quickly finished writing orders on another patient's chart and dropped it into the "Orders" box. In the days before computerized charts, when things were busy and no one was readily available to receive orders on a patient, the physician would write them on the patient's chart and drop the chart into one of several slots in an "Orders" box located on the countertop. As soon as a nurse was available, he or she would pick up the next chart and begin to carry out the orders on the patient.

I grabbed the chart for Room 2 and promptly headed that way. Burns can be terribly painful. While many folks in the ER may be experiencing some type of discomfort, there are differing levels of pain. Second-degree burns can be one of the most severe types of pain, and relief from that pain is a high priority for treatment.

As I entered Room 2, I found my patient, Mr. Morris, lying in the opposite direction from what I normally would encounter. His head was closest to the door, so I didn't see his face initially. His wife was standing next to the stretcher on the right side, her face clearly registering concern and perhaps a degree of distress as she held her husband's hand in hers.

I greeted her first. "Hello, my name is Dr. Grant, Tom Grant. How are you?" I reached out to shake hands with her, after which I walked around to the other side of the stretcher to greet her husband. He introduced himself as he lay flat on his back, "Hi, I'm Roger Morris."

After looking him in the eyes as we met, I glanced at the rest of his body, searching for the area of burn. He seemed quite composed for someone with a serious burn. Usually, for patients with second-degree burns, it is difficult for them to keep from moaning in pain.

Mr. Morris swiftly responded to my nonverbal query, "It's on the bottom of my feet." He pointed down to the other end of the stretcher. Now I understood why Linda had reversed the normal patient position on the stretcher—she didn't want anyone accidentally bumping into Mr. Morris's injury as they entered the room.

The bottom of one's feet is an unusual place to get serious burns, especially when dressed like Mr. Morris, who was wearing slacks, a lightly starched white broadcloth shirt, and a nice-looking tie.

In the brief instant it took for me to walk to the end of the stretcher, my mind began running through possible causes for a burn in that location. At the top of the list would be a chemical burn, but that was typically found in people working with alkali substances, such as pouring concrete. Next would be thermal burns from accidentally stepping barefoot onto a very hot object not seen by the patient or, perhaps, unintentionally stepping into very hot water or another liquid.

Neither of those options seemed likely in Mr. Morris's case due to his attire. I was certain he didn't suffer the injury and then get cleaned up and put on a tie and slacks just to come to the emergency room!

When I arrived at his feet, I saw saline-soaked gauze sponges Linda had placed over the burns. She had also slightly elevated his feet. Both of those simple actions help to diminish the pain and retard the associated swelling that would develop. Lifting a few of the gauze sponges to inspect the bottom of his feet revealed an ugly site.

Multiple fluid-filled blisters about one-half to three-quarters of an inch in diameter were present, along with substantial redness over most of the bottom of his feet. There were also a few patches of pale-white skin, suggesting the possibility of some very deep and more serious burns, classified as third-degree burns. Only the back couple of inches of his heels were spared from burns.

When I first looked at Mr. Morris's feet, I couldn't help but be awed by how calm and collected he was. The burns must have been extremely painful, yet he had been pleasant without indicating how uncomfortable he must be.

On the way to the room, I had looked at Mr. Morris's chart for a list of allergies, knowing I would give him an injection of pain medicine as soon as possible. He had none.

"Mr. Morris, are you allergic to anything…any medications?" I asked. Doctors and nurses frequently repeat this question to patients, just in case the patient initially forgot about something, especially when they are in pain. Or, sometimes a family member may arrive and is able to provide additional information.

"No, sir," he said in his remarkably composed voice, although as I looked at him, I noticed perspiration on his forehead and his heart monitor revealed a rate above one hundred, most likely from the pain he was experiencing.

"This may sound silly, but are these burns causing you a lot of pain?" I asked. I knew that certain underlying diseases, like diabetes, could cause deterioration in the function of the nerves in the feet, resulting in a partial or complete loss of the ability to feel pain, which is a very important protective mechanism. Such a condition is referred to as a neuropathy. I doubted that was the case, but I needed to be sure.

"Yes, sir, they are hurting," he said, still with great poise. Most people with this type of burn would be crying, or even screaming from pain, unless they had already taken something before coming to the ER. Linda had documented in his chart that was not the case—not even Tylenol or Motrin.

Before continuing with Mr. Morris's history and physical examination, I asked Linda to go ahead and get him a dose of an injectable narcotic mixed with an anti-nausea medicine to help ease his pain ASAP.

"Mr. Morris, while Linda is getting your pain medicine, I'm going to test the sensation on the bottom of your feet. If you feel me touch you, please tell me if it seems sharp like a pinprick or dull like a Q-tip," which just happened to be what I was using to test his sensation.

"OK?" I asked.

"Yes, sir," he replied.

This was a common method for determining the depth, or seriousness, of injury for burns. If the patient feels a sharp sensation, it means that the burn has gone through part of the outer layers of skin but the nerve fibers are still intact—thus, one feels the sharp pain sensation.

On the other hand, if the burn goes through the deeper layers of skin, it can destroy the nerve fibers in that area and there will be a lack of sharp sensation. In such a setting, a person may only feel the dullness of pressure from nerve fibers further down in the tissue.

"Sharp or dull?" I asked as I began to test the burned area covering much of the soles of his feet, sparing only his heels. A good portion of his response was "dull," mixed in with a less frequent response of "sharp." That was very concerning. I stood up from my bent-over position.

"I'm afraid you have some very serious burns to your feet that may require skin grafting." I looked to Mr. Morris and his wife as I spoke. "If the burned tissue forms scars, then it can impair the function of your feet. We will also need to watch closely for any early signs of infection."

Linda came in with the pain medicine and prepared to administer it as I continued. "I need to call the plastic surgeon who takes care of these types of burns and let him know about your injury. But first, please tell me how this happened. From the pattern and type of burns on your feet, I don't have any idea how this occurred, except that whatever you came in contact with was very, very hot."

The initial response from Mr. and Mrs. Morris was a few moments of silence. As I looked to Mr. Morris, he looked to his wife as if he were saying to her, *Do you want to tell him or should I?* I could see on her face that he would tell the story.

"I walked across a bed of hot coals," he said briefly as he looked me straight in the eye. He held that look for a few seconds and then glanced away, now staring toward his injured feet. His wife looked over to me as she put her hand on his shoulder.

Caught off guard by his response, I wasn't certain I'd heard him correctly. "Excuse me?" I said as I slightly turned my head to make sure I could hear clearly.

Mrs. Morris now spoke. "He walked across a bed of hot coals. He was attending a seminar on faith."

As she spoke, I could see the faint appearance of anguish on her face, although it was largely overshadowed by the love she clearly had for her husband, evident in her nonverbal communication. It seemed to me her unspoken assessment was that he had made a bad decision, but she still loved and supported him.

I wasn't quite sure how to respond. My first thought was to get an idea about the amount of time involved in exposure to help determine the extent of the injury. "What kind of distance are we talking about?" I asked as I made every effort to appear nonjudgmental.

Mr. Morris now looked up at me again. "About eight feet, I would say." He paused for a second, and as he glanced down at his feet, he added, "I guess my faith just wasn't strong enough." That last comment was spoken softly and I almost didn't hear it. His wife gently patted him on the shoulder as tears began to pool in her eyes.

I hated to hear that doubt and despair in his voice. I walked back down to the end of the stretcher where his feet were. "I don't think it was a lack of faith that caused your feet to get burned, Mr. Morris. I think it was more likely a lack of thick skin or proper protection."

I made that comment from an analytical perspective rather than a religious one, and then realized how it might have sounded. It wasn't my intent to challenge or offend my patient or his wife. I was afraid I may have precipitated a more nuanced and delicate conversation.

"What do you mean?" Mr. Morris asked. He didn't appear offended, judging by the tone of his voice, only curious. I hesitated for a moment and then decided to continue the conversation.

"Well, some people who walk across hot coals do so by means other than faith. Some people gradually build up thick layers of callous over time by repetitively exposing their feet to injurious agents such as heat, chemicals, etc. Their feet still get burned when they cross the coals, but it is the callous, which is dead skin, that gets burned rather than living tissue—such as in your case."

I could see on his face I had caused him to think about his situation for a moment. I continued, "Some put a layer of ointment on the bottom of their feet that actually reflects heat and decreases the amount of thermal energy their feet get exposed to when they walk on the coals."

I looked at the bottom of his feet as I spoke and waited for a response before I looked back at him. All I received was silence. When I eventually looked up, Mr. Morris and his wife were exchanging glances. I didn't feel as though I had insulted their faith, and I hoped it provided them additional insight into such activities.

"Before the pain medicine Linda gave you starts to fully kick in, let's talk about your care going forward. I'm pretty certain the plastic surgeon is going to want to admit you to the hospital, where we can control your pain as much as possible, keep you off your feet while elevating them, remove some of the dead skin as it declares itself, and teach you and your wife how to change the bandages." I wanted them both to have a chance to understand and ask questions before the pain medicine started to make Mr. Morris groggy.

"Any questions before I call the plastic surgeon?" I asked as I looked to both of them for a response. They glanced at each other and then back at me, and both shook their heads in the negative.

I got up from the stool and let them know I would return once I had talked with the surgeon. I reached out to shake Mr. Morris's hand, knowing he would probably be sleeping when I came back. I wanted to offer him a piece of advice before he drifted off. I held on to his hand and looked into his eyes.

"Faith is a wonderful gift, and growing in one's faith can provide many great blessings," I said as I momentarily reflected upon my own life.

"However, the next time someone wants to demonstrate their faith—*and yours*—through some seemingly miraculous means, please encourage them to do so in a manner that doesn't jeopardize anyone's health." I paused for a moment.

"Perhaps consider walking on water instead," I said as I smiled at him and his wife.

They both smiled back and Mr. Morris replied, "Thanks, Doc, I'll keep that in mind next time."

As I turned and headed toward the door, an additional thought popped into my mind. I spun around and added, "And please be sure the water is shallow."

We all smiled, and Mr. Morris gave me the thumbs-up.

Unspoken

"Can I see my family first?" he asked in a very composed and polite manner. His question made me feel as though I were a judge who had passed a sentence on him, and before he was taken away, he requested to see his loved ones.

He had come into the emergency room complaining of chest pain. Anna, one of the experienced and very astute ER nurses, recognized right away that he appeared ill and might abruptly deteriorate, so she placed him in Room 2, one of the major resuscitation rooms—just in case. That kind of forethought could greatly facilitate his care should he suddenly become unstable.

Anna called for me as soon as the patient was in the room and hurriedly began the initial treatment and precautions taken for all chest-pain patients. Anna knew his complaint could be caused by one of many life-threatening situations such as a heart attack (MI, or myocardial infarction), a blood clot to the lungs (pulmonary embolism), a collapsed lung (pneumothorax), a rent or tear in a major blood vessel (aortic dissection), or one of several other very serious conditions.

As I entered the room, I immediately saw the reason for Anna's concern. Our patient was ashen in color with a faint degree of sweat (diaphoresis) upon his skin. His breathing rate was also increased above normal. To any reasonably competent clinician, he clearly was in serious distress.

"Hello, Mr. Overton. My name is Dr. Grant," I said without betraying my concern for his condition. I walked to the side of the stretcher and gently grasped his outstretched hand.

Anna promptly corrected me with information she had gained in her minute or two with the patient before my arrival. "Dr. Grant, this is *Dr.* Overton. He is a retired neurosurgeon." She knew that fact would facilitate the conversation between doctor and doctor-patient.

Anna had spoken without looking up as she connected the IV tubing from the bag hanging on the IV pole to the Angiocath now situated in a vein in Dr. Overton's left forearm. Anna was working diligently to accomplish the initial measures needed on every seriously ill patient—obtaining vital signs, placing the patient on oxygen, putting him on cardiac and oxygen saturation monitors, drawing blood for labs, and starting an IV.

As I asked Dr. Overton several questions about his chest pain, the EKG technician came into the room and began putting the sticky leads onto his chest wall and extremities to measure the electrical activity of his heart. As Frank ran the EKG, I listened to Dr. Overton's responses to my questions and collected as much physical information as I could just by observing him.

He spoke in a melodic, soothing voice. He appeared to be about sixty-five years of age with prominent facial features and silver-gray hair, making him very distinguished in appearance. He was slender and looked as though he was in good physical condition.

I didn't need to ask many questions—he knew what information was important, as he offered answers to questions I hadn't yet asked. I could tell he had only recently retired.

He had developed intermittent chest pain over the last six months, and it had progressively worsened. He had made an appointment with his family physician but postponed it until after he returned from the vacation he was currently enjoying with his family. He came from Virginia and was in town visiting their two sons.

Forty minutes before arriving at the ER, his pain had returned, becoming constant and very severe. In addition, his breathing had become more labored, and he knew it would not subside without medical treatment. He confessed to himself what he had suspected all along but refused to believe—that the pain in his chest was probably due to heart disease.

Even before the EKG finished printing, it was clear his tracing showed evidence of a large heart attack over the front portion of his heart. And after listening to his lungs and examining his neck veins, it was clear that Dr. Overton was also in acute heart failure, his heart not able to provide the necessary blood flow containing oxygen and nutrients to the rest of his body. This was a very ominous finding in the context of his history and his EKG results, something he likely knew himself.

"Let's go ahead and give you another nitroglycerin tablet," I said as I reached out to drop the small tablet under his tongue. Anna had previously administered one by protocol before I had entered the room.

"Let's see if it has any impact on your pain," I commented after giving him the medication. "Of course, we will be keeping a close eye on your blood pressure also."

The rapid sequence and simultaneous nature of activities that began with his arrival continued. Radiology technicians were now in the room taking a chest X-ray while laboratory personnel were collecting the tubes of blood and respiratory therapy was increasing the oxygen concentration flowing into the mask covering his mouth and nose. Alleviating his chest pain and improving the oxygen content in his bloodstream were top priorities.

Several minutes passed without improvement in his chest pain from the nitroglycerin, so I administered several milligrams of morphine sulfate through his IV line. I knew I had to be very judicious in the amount of medication I gave him because his blood pressure continued to be at the lower border of normal. Pain medications like morphine, as well as nitroglycerin, can sometimes decrease a person's blood pressure, which could significantly worsen the overall condition of a patient with a heart attack.

"What do you think, Dr. Grant?" he asked, reading the concern on my face as I watched his EKG monitor that displayed his cardiac rhythm and the oxygen saturation monitor that continually measured the amount of oxygen carried in his bloodstream. His oxygen content was now at the lower edge of normal.

"Well, Dr. Overton, it's as you suspected. You are indeed having an MI." I tried not to sound anxious as I related the information to him, even though, in my mind, I knew he was in a critical and potentially very unstable condition.

His prognosis was not good. Heart attacks involving the front part of the heart typically result in more muscle damage than ones in other areas. The increased amount of heart damage makes it more difficult for the heart to adequately pump blood to the rest of the body.

In Dr. Overton's case, this was evidenced by his borderline low BP and his falling oxygen content. The inability to adequately pump blood causes fluid to weep into the small air sacs in his lungs (alveoli), making it harder for oxygen to enter the blood cells that flow through the small blood vessels (capillaries) in the lungs.

Dr. Overton's current condition would require us to walk a fine line with the treatment we provided. His ER visit came at a time before the use of "clot buster" drugs and rapid cardiac catheterizations with stent placement, which are so common today, and which provide much better therapeutic options. The treatments available at the time of his visit were much more limited.

"How's the pain after that last dose of morphine?" I asked as I stepped beyond the head end of his stretcher, closer to the wall where the monitors were mounted. Having left his field of vision, I began assembling emergency equipment that might be needed if his heart suddenly stopped or if the oxygen content in his blood continued to drop.

I kept the conversation going both to assess his level of pain while also attempting to distract him from what I was doing, hoping to minimize any anxiety that might develop. Anxiety increases one's heart rate, which puts more demand on the heart and its need for oxygen.

"It's about a five," he answered, having been an eight on the one-to-ten scale before the nitroglycerin and morphine were administered.

While his pain had improved with the drugs, it still persisted, and the oxygen content in his blood was falling further. This meant his heart was not getting the oxygen it needed to do its job, causing it to fail further, creating a vicious cycle. It was like running a marathon but without any fluid replenishment or source of energy. One would become progressively less and less capable of continuing.

In a calm and steady voice, I told Dr. Overton that I would like to assist his breathing for a few minutes to diminish his body's work of breathing while also increasing his oxygen content. I explained that the positive pressure I provided with the BVM could help increase the oxygen content in his blood and potentially decrease his chest pain further. That could help improve some of the heart failure he was experiencing.

Assisting someone's breathing in this situation is not an easy task for the patient or the clinician. Putting a mask over the face of a patient who is having difficulty breathing can be a frightening sensation. It can feel very restrictive and cause them to panic. And if the physician doesn't time the compression of the bag as it forces air into the patient's lungs in concert with the patient's effort to draw air in, it can disrupt their breathing pattern and cause them to feel as if they can't get enough air. It is a delicate dance between two partners.

In the very brief period of time we had been together—perhaps fifteen minutes, at this point—it seemed as though we had formed a mutual trust that made it easier to work together. I knew I was asking him to allow me to do something that could cause him distress, but he also knew it could be of benefit and he was committed to cooperating in whatever way he could.

I stood at the head of the stretcher, beyond the top of his head, but leaned forward so he could see my face. He was familiar with a BVM, which was connected to 100 percent oxygen. Almost all physicians have used a BVM at some point in their medical career.

I watched his pattern of breathing so my mind would be in sync with the rate and depth of each breath. As I did so, I explained what I was about to do. He understood. As he began exhaling, I put the mask over his mouth and nose, and just as he began to breathe in, I squeezed the bag, assisting his inhalation as I forced air into his lungs. I stopped squeezing just before he began to breathe out so I did not impede his exhalation.

Thankfully, we turned out to be good dance partners. As we did this over the next several minutes, the oxygen content in his blood improved, increasing from 88 to 93 percent, which was a significant improvement even though it was still below normal for his age.

I took the mask off his face to give him a break and to assess whether it helped his symptoms. He said it had improved his breathing and also decreased his chest pain.

While that was good news, it also confirmed what I had anticipated—he would need to be intubated. That process would involve the insertion of a tube through his mouth and into his airway (trachea) so we could better control the ventilation or breathing process. It also provided the ability to maintain the assisted breathing for extended periods of time, through the use of a ventilator.

It wasn't long before the oxygen content displayed on his monitor began to decrease again and Dr. Overton's chest pain began to worsen despite additional morphine.

Once again, I placed the mask over his face and helped to manually blow oxygen into his lungs. Once again, he cooperated completely with my efforts. His oxygen saturation increased back into the normal range, and his chest pain decreased in intensity once again.

It was time for him to be intubated. As I continued to bag him, I explained to him that it looked as though we would need to intubate him and described how we would go about doing that.

While he had seen many patients in the operating room intubated by the anesthesiologist prior to the surgery he was about to perform, I explained this situation would be different.

We would not be able to administer the drugs they often use to put the patient to sleep because those drugs could drop his blood pressure, which would worsen his heart attack or cause his heart to beat erratically, or even stop.

Still, however, we would give him a drug to sedate him and make him comfortable, although not make him completely unconscious. I explained the procedure to him, and he nodded in affirmation.

I took the bag and mask away from his face to see if he had any questions before we proceeded.

It was then he made his request.

"May I please see my family first before we do this?" he asked. His question made me realize what he was thinking. He knew there was the possibility it could be his last chance to ever talk to them. Once the tube was placed into his trachea, he would not be able to speak until it was removed. But it could only be removed if the amount of fluid in his lungs decreased and the amount of oxygen in his blood improved. It could save his life, or he could continue to deteriorate despite the effort to treat his condition.

Although I knew time was of the essence in this situation where his status could suddenly worsen at any moment, it was a request no one could deny him.

"Certainly," I said as I motioned for Anna to get his wife and sons from the waiting room. I placed the mask back over his mouth and nose to assist his breathing as much as possible before he spoke with his family. That would make him as comfortable as possible during the time he talked with them.

I asked Kevin, the experienced respiratory therapist in the room with us, to continue assisting Dr. Overton's breathing as I stepped out of the room and into the hallway. There, I communicated to Dr. Overton's family the gravity of his current condition and explained what we needed to do in an effort to improve it. I wanted to first give them the news and provide them with a few moments to regain their composure. Then I led them into the room.

I motioned for Kevin to remove the mask. I nodded for him to temporarily leave the room as I moved toward some equipment near the head of the bed off to one side. I tried to provide them as much privacy as possible while I continued to watch the monitors over the head of the bed. I was uncomfortable leaving Dr. Overton's bedside because of the critical nature of his condition.

Even though this was a very personal moment, I didn't feel as though my presence was too intrusive.

Despite his condition and the symptoms he was experiencing, Dr. Overton smiled at them as they entered the room.

"Mary, it will be OK, please don't be upset," he said in a soft and gentle voice as he raised his right hand for her. She moved from the foot of the stretcher to his side, taking his hand in hers. They looked at each other in silence for several moments as they held hands. She struggled to smile at him as tears streamed down her face.

"Mitch, Alan, take care of your mother for me," he said as he shifted his gaze from Mary to their sons, who stood at the foot of the bed. His sons nodded in affirmation, tears tracking their faces also.

Then there was a long pause as Mary continued to hold his hand. I felt as though I knew the words he wanted to say next, but they did not come. Tears welled up in my own eyes. I imagined he wanted to tell them all how much he loved them, but he didn't. Perhaps it wasn't his manner to say it. Perhaps they could clearly read it in his eyes. Either way, I hoped he would say it. We both knew there was a very good chance he would not have another opportunity.

He didn't though.

After a few more moments, Dr. Overton spoke to me. It may have been because he could feel the need for more oxygen or his chest pain was increasing. Or maybe the thought of separation from the family he deeply loved was too difficult for him to continue to consider.

"OK, Dr. Grant, I'm ready when you are," he said as he shifted his gaze from the eyes of his wife to me. I asked his wife and sons to go back to the waiting room and I let them know I would talk with them as soon as we were finished.

Once they left the room, Kevin reentered and I began the procedure. Anna was also with us to administer the medications as I ordered them. The oxygen content in his bloodstream had already fallen significantly during the brief conversation. The intubation procedure was performed without difficulty. Once the tube was in position, I gave Dr. Overton additional medication to cause him to sleep so he would not struggle against the tube, allowing him to rest comfortably.

With the tube in place, the oxygen content in his bloodstream began to rise and reached acceptable levels very quickly. In addition, his blood pressure improved and he appeared to be more stable. I felt that the decision had been a good therapeutic choice and quite possibly a life-saving action.

I was cautiously optimistic about his chances now. I knew others might not have been as aggressive in treating his condition, or might have hesitated in intubating a patient under these circumstances.

Shortly after completing the procedure and connecting Dr. Overton to the ventilator, the cardiologist arrived, having been called earlier when I had first seen the initial EKG. In conferring with Dave, the cardiologist, he agreed with our treatment and was pleased we had intubated Dr. Overton when we did.

Dave went with Dr. Overton as they moved him upstairs to the Coronary Care Unit (CCU). I was able to briefly talk to Dr. Overton's family before they, too, went upstairs. I explained that the procedure had gone well and his condition had begun to improve.

A couple of hours later, my twelve-hour shift in the emergency department ended, and I headed home to get some rest before returning for my next shift in about ten hours. I eagerly anticipated hearing about Dr. Overton's progress once I returned.

The next day's shift in the ED started busy at seven a.m. It wasn't until later in the evening after my shift ended that I was able to go up to the CCU to check on Dr. Overton's progress. Despite the draining day of work, my spirits were uplifted as I thought about Dr. Overton and his family. I felt certain the improvement we had witnessed in the ER the day before would have continued throughout the day.

As with most CCUs, the lights were low with the constant chirp of various monitors and alarms throughout the area. I navigated my way to the central nursing station in the middle of the CCU to see which room Dr. Overton was in.

Lori, one of the outstanding CCU nurses, looked up from the desk where she was sitting. "Which patient are you looking for, Dr. Grant?" she asked.

"Dr. Overton. He was an admission from the ED late yesterday afternoon," I said, anxious to see him and his family.

But Lori's facial expression alerted me I would not hear the news I hoped for. In that flash of a second, I expected to hear that Dr. Overton's progress had plateaued, requiring additional medications and adjustments to the ventilator settings that supported his breathing. That would mean a longer stay in the CCU.

Instead, the news was unanticipated and devastating. "I'm sorry, Dr. Grant, but Dr. Overton passed away this morning."

She paused for just a moment. "His MI extended"—grew bigger in size—"and his heart failure worsened. He arrested and they couldn't get him back." Her face reflected the pain she knew I felt from hearing the news. "I'm very sorry."

My heart sank. I thought we had helped Dr. Overton turn the corner in his disease process, and that he would live to spend more time with the family he clearly loved, and who loved him. But it wasn't to be.

He never had another chance to talk to his wife and children. The tube we put in to help him breathe was not removed until after his death. The last words they had shared together were the ones spoken in the emergency room. No doubt, Dr. Overton anticipated that might be the case.

I felt heartbroken for his family and wished I could have spoken with them to let them know how much he desired to share those last words with them despite his difficulty breathing and the agonizing chest pain he was experiencing. In his dire and tenuous condition, his thoughts were of them.

As I slowly drove home through the darkened streets that night, I thought again of how fragile life is, and how every moment is a gift we must cherish, especially with those we love.

Christmas Conundrum

It was getting close to Christmas, and the air outside was cold and brisk. White clouds came out of one's mouth when speaking to anyone outdoors. The skies had become heavily overcast, and it appeared as if it would snow any minute.

I ran to the emergency room from my car. The thin cloth of my scrubs didn't keep my legs very warm in weather like this, so I covered the hundred yards between my car and the ER rather hastily, even though it was only six forty-five a.m.

"Kinda cold, Dr. Grant?" was my greeting from Emma, one of the night nurses, as I came through the sliding glass doors of the emergency room ambulance entrance.

"Just a tad!" I answered as I hopped up and down, trying to generate some body heat. I then headed to the small ER physicians' office, where I stowed my briefcase and picked up my stethoscope.

After coming out of the office, I listened to the tales from the night doc who was going off shift. He informed me that it had been unusually quiet after two thirty a.m., probably because of the cold weather outside. After some additional small talk, he bundled up and headed out the doors. I made a beeline for the hot chocolate.

As I stood in our little coffee room next to the nursing desk and chart rack, about to pour milk into the instant hot chocolate mix, I saw one of the nurses escorting a bundled-up family of three from the waiting room to ER Room 1. At about that same time, one of the registration clerks brought back a chart and dropped it into the "To Be Seen" portion of the chart rack.

"Not even seven fifteen a.m. yet and already a patient," I moaned to myself. I preferred to warm up and wake up before I started seeing patients.

I hesitated with the hot chocolate mix. *No sense in making hot chocolate if I go see a patient and it gets cold waiting for me.* Hot chocolate is only good if it's hot—cold is not so hot.

Maybe the case will be straightforward and only take a few minutes, like a suture removal, I thought. I kept the milk in hand as I walked out of the coffee room and over to the chart rack. I picked up the chart and looked for the box on the sheet titled "Chief Complaint."

As I searched for the info, I hoped it wouldn't be a vague complaint that oftentimes has no answer and may require a lengthy workup, such as "hurting all over," "weak for the last six months," or "just not feeling right." A lot of times, it seemed as though one could predict how the day would go just by looking at the chief complaint on that first chart of the shift.

Then I saw it: "Toy stuck in mouth." Now that was a new one for me. In fourteen years of emergency medicine, I had never run across that one before. I had tackled items stuck in the nose and ears but not a toy lodged in the mouth.

Immediately, in my mind's eye, I envisioned a little child with rosy cheeks wearing a big red fireman's hat who then began to grin, revealing a large red fire engine lodged horizontally in his mouth where his teeth normally would be. That brought a smile to my face.

My mind then abruptly replaced that vision with one of a toy Rudolph the Red-Nosed Reindeer standing inside the little boy's widely opened mouth with its head and antlers extending outside the boy's lips. Rudolph's nose was brightly blinking SOS in Morse code, accompanied by a look of anguish on the reindeer's face.

At about that same time, one of the nurses rounded the corner and I handed the chart to her. "We have a rather unusual case," I said as she took the chart from my hand and proceeded to read the chief complaint herself.

"Oh, boy!" Brenda said, as she looked up at me and smiled. "This ought to be real exciting, especially since he is only two years old. I'm sure he'll fully cooperate with us." She, too, was grinning from ear to ear. I started to visualize the fire truck again, but this time, it was in *her* mouth.

"Right," I said as she turned and headed toward ER Room 1, where our patient waited. I put the milk back in the fridge and headed for the same destination. After all, hot chocolate should be savored on cold days like this, not gulped down in a hurry.

As soon as I entered Room 1, I could see that it was not a fire engine, and definitely not Rudolph.

Across the room from me were Mom and Dad, both standing next to the stretcher with their two-year-old son, Jonathan Wells, comfortably resting in Dad's arms. He was one of the cutest children I have ever seen. He was all bundled up in his little brown coat that was furry white inside with a hood attached at the collar. It covered the top of his head, leaving visible a cherub face with rosy-red cheeks and locks of curly blond hair. Through his open coat, you could see his long-sleeved red shirt and his blue jeans. Topping it all off were his bright-red tennis shoes.

As cute as he was, however, all those features were not what I noticed first. Between his ruby-colored lips was a bright golden globe that gleamed at me from across the room. His mouth was held widely open by the globe, revealing a circle of metallic color that made me think of the Jaws character from the James Bond movie.

The poor child's face looked comical—somewhat like a large mouth bass with a giant golden lure stuck inside of it.

At first, I was amazed the child wasn't sobbing, but I soon realized his mouth was so stretched out and filled by the golden globe that he could barely even whimper. At that point, I smiled as I wondered if the parents might want to keep it in for a while.

As I crossed the room toward the family, I spoke to Mom and Dad: "Mr. and Mrs. Wells, I'm Dr. Grant. It looks like you have a rather surprising problem here." I shook hands with them both as Dad began to speak.

"We weren't quite sure where to go for help," Mr. Wells explained in a somewhat sheepish fashion.

I nodded my head in an affirmative manner as I tried to closely study the golden glow coming from their child's mouth.

"We think it may be a knob that came off of something," Mrs. Wells said. "I have no idea how he got that thing in his mouth, and we couldn't figure out how to get it out."

"We were afraid of pushing it in further and shutting off his air, so we brought him in," Mr. Wells added. Both Mr. and Mrs. Wells had rather hopeless looks on their faces. They appeared to both be very reasonable parents who were not frantic and were almost apologetic for having to come to the ER for this problem.

As I continued to sneak peeks at the little guy in Dad's arms I couldn't help but think of the pig at a Hawaiian luau, the one with an apple in its mouth. This child's mouth was open as wide as it would go, and the surface of the globe was very smooth and shiny, due in part to the fact that it was covered in saliva. Unfortunately, that meant it was as slippery as it was shiny.

As I stood there thinking about how we could go about getting this globe out, I couldn't help but smile—what a predicament.

Instantly, however, my amusement turned to serious concern. Jonathan started to make a slight choking sound, and I suddenly realized that he was having difficulty swallowing his own saliva. With his mouth open that wide, he wasn't able to adequately swallow, causing his secretions to potentially drain into his airway rather than being swallowed into the stomach.

I quickly took Jonathan out of Dad's arms and tilted his head down as I rested the remainder of his body on my forearm, his chin nestled in my hand as he faced the floor. This put him at about a forty-five-degree angle to the ground. As I did so, I spoke to Dad, trying to maintain a calm tone of voice. "Dad, let's tilt him upside down so he won't choke on his saliva while we think about how to get this out."

I then instructed Dad to have a seat on the stretcher next to us and handed Jonathan back to him, keeping the boy in a head-down position with the front portion of Jonathan's body resting on Dad's forearm, which lay against his thigh as he sat on the stretcher.

Now that Jonathan's airway was protected to some degree by gravity, I had a little more time to think about how to get it out. I was trying to decide what instrument I could use to slip around and behind it to try to pry it out when Dad spoke again.

"There may be a hole somewhere on the ball, but we couldn't turn it to find out where it was." Again, that helpless look appeared on Dad's face, perhaps more prominent than before.

"Good idea," I said as I picked up a pair of rubber gloves. "Brenda, will you get me a straight hemostat please?" Now, at least, I had a plan of action. I thought that if I could gently wipe the saliva off the metallic globe without applying too much pressure, I could then get enough traction with the rubber glove to carefully rotate the globe until we could find the hole, assuming there was one.

I sat down on the floor beneath Jonathan, who remained in his dad's arms at the forty-five-degree downward angle. Brenda handed me the hemostat, a medical instrument that looks somewhat like a very skinny pair of scissors but acts a lot like a pair of needle-nose pliers.

After gently wiping the saliva from the front surface of the golden globe, I used my gloved fingers to carefully rotate the globe little by little until a small circular opening eventually appeared. It rolled fairly easily, almost like a ball bearing in some type of machine. The globe seemed to be the perfect size, fitting snuggly between the child's set of teeth in the upper and lower jaw.

Jonathan never whimpered, he just studied me intently with his big blue eyes. He never struggled or became frantic. He was like an injured animal that remains still when someone tries to help it, as if he understood I was trying to make things better for him.

As I continued to sit on the floor beneath Jonathan, I took the hemostat and put the tips inside the hole in the globe. I was able to open the tips wide enough to apply some force against the inner edges of the hole in the globe. With this tenuous grasp on the globe, I gently but firmly pulled back on the globe until it literally popped out of Jonathan's mouth. Jonathan's face immediately displayed a look of astonishment! Of course, mine probably did also.

"Dad, you can raise him up now," I said as I hopped up off the floor with the prized golden globe still on the hemostat in my hand. Dad lifted Jonathan up with both hands, bringing him eye to eye with everyone as he held him to his chest, one arm wrapped around him.

Jonathan's look of astonishment persisted, his rosy-red cheeks still filled with color. He first looked at his mother standing to his left and then to his dad, and then back at me. After a momentary pause in which he seemed to be gathering his bearings, he abruptly decided to test his lungs and promptly filled the ER with wails that I'm sure sounded like music to Mom and Dad. They certainly were to me!

After he cleared his lungs a little, I checked his jaw, mouth, and lungs to ensure things were OK. No damage had been done in the course of Jonathan's holiday activity. I then headed for the door, pausing as I reached it, considering one last discharge instruction for the parents.

"You may wish to keep him away from the Christmas tree ornaments this season!"

I smiled and headed back to my hot chocolate as they all waved goodbye.

Different Times, Different Worlds

It was a busy Friday night, as usual. Multiple docs were on shift in the emergency room, and it was my turn to work the "Suture Room."

This ER was large with about twenty-four patient rooms, including a very large room near the rear of the emergency department known as the Suture Room. A stretcher was placed in each corner of the room with the front beds separated from the back beds by a segmented wall of cabinets and shelves containing various supplies. This storage partition was on each side of the room with a walkway between them, allowing one to easily access the front and back beds.

It worked well to have a single location in which the various types of wound care instruments and materials could be stored to address the many kinds of injuries—abrasions, puncture wounds, small burns, lacerations, animal or human bites, etc. The room had a high-powered overhead light for each of the four beds, which greatly facilitated one's ability to clean the wound, debride it (remove badly damaged or dead tissue), and repair it.

The layout also created greater efficiency in patient care by bringing together individuals who needed similar treatment. If there were several lacerations, the physician could examine one patient's wound, numb it with a local anesthetic, and then go see the next patient while the nurse would clean and prep the anesthetized wound, set up the necessary instruments, and get it ready for repair. Occasionally, someone would need to go for an X-ray, which would temporarily bump them out of the room until they returned. The overall process usually ran very smoothly.

That evening, there was a constant stream of patients with wounds in need of care, many of which were lacerations that would undergo the described process. In evenings, there usually weren't as many animal bites, construction injuries (especially nail guns or power-saw injuries), or falls from bikes or skateboards.

The steady flow of wounded patients was not overwhelming. It had an ebb and flow in which we might fall behind for a while but soon thereafter catch up. The wounds that required the greatest amount of time and effort were typically facial lacerations that necessitated a more delicate and sometimes layered repair to minimize the potential for scarring.

At about ten o'clock, I was nearly finished suturing a laceration on the arm of an elderly lady, Mrs. Hudson. An hour or so earlier, her daughter, who appeared to be in her midforties, had brought the sweet woman in. Mrs. Hudson had injured her left arm at home where she covered the wound with a sterile bandage and wrapped it against her arm with a short roll of gauze.

When I initially talked to the elderly woman, asking what happened and how she had received the cut, she apologized for taking up my time.

I smiled at her as I said, "You've made my evening. I would have been here without anything to do if you hadn't come to visit me."

She managed a slight smile in return and replied, "I'm sure you have a lot of other people who are really sick and need your attention much more than me." Her appearance and mannerisms reminded me of Aunt May from the Spider-Man movie.

Her daughter, Sally, appeared to have come from work, wearing a handsome long-sleeved jacket, blouse, and pleated skirt—all different shades of a golden-brown color, complementing the hue of her shoulder-length hair. The pearls around her neck seemed to be the perfect accent.

As Mrs. Hudson finished speaking, Sally added, "She didn't want me to bring her, but I glanced at it and it seems like a serious cut to me." Sally briefly looked at her mom and smiled as she continued. "She fell from the step stool as she reached for an item in an upper cabinet. She must have hit her arm on the edge of something in the kitchen. When I came by, she had already wrapped it up and was cleaning blood off the floor."

The elderly woman in her early eighties responded in a soft voice, "It's really not anything that needs a doctor's attention. I think it would probably do fine." She followed her words with a pleasant expression, just like Aunt May would have done.

I love older folks like Mrs. Hudson. Their generation saw a great deal of hardship including the Dust Bowl, the Great Depression, Prohibition, World War II, and the Korean War. Their childhoods often included cooking and heating from a wood-fire stove, water from a well in the ground, and challenging environmental conditions. Their transportation when they were young was often by horse and wagon unless they were well-to-do. They might have had electricity for light in the evenings, or perhaps gas lamps, kerosene lanterns, fireplaces, or just candles. It was a pretty tough and self-sufficient generation.

"Well, since you've taken the opportunity to come see me, how about I look at it while you're here. Would that be OK?" I asked with a smile. It was hard to tell from her weathered and wrinkled face, but along with her slight tilt of the head, I think she may have blushed just a tad.

"If you think it necessary, that would be fine," she said in her quiet voice. Before unwrapping the bandage, I first asked if she had hurt herself anywhere else, and although she replied in the negative, I still examined her from head to toe to make sure we didn't miss anything. All else seemed fine.

I carefully removed her bandage to discover a gently curved, flap-type four-inch laceration that was moderately deep. It was located on the top side of her left forearm. It also had some bruising around it.

"It doesn't look that bad, does it, Doctor?" she queried, almost at the same time that her daughter softly gasped. I'm sure in the enhanced lighting of the Suture Room, the wound looked significantly worse than it had at her mom's house.

For a moment, I imagined what this woman must have experienced in her life. Although she had a wound that clearly needed attention, from her perspective, it wasn't really that bad. And she wasn't saying this because her vision was poor or because she was afraid of the actual care we might provide. In her mind, this substantial wound just didn't warrant the attention of a doctor—it could be cared for at home.

"Well, I think it's good that you came in this evening," I said to her as I looked her in the eyes. "I do believe this is going to require quite a few stitches to put back together. I'm glad your daughter encouraged you to visit us—that was a wise decision." I briefly looked away from the elderly woman to give her daughter a wink as she grinned and nodded her head outside the vision of her mother.

I proceeded to tell Mrs. Hudson how we would go about numbing the wound and then cleaning it and putting it back together. The sweet lady replied, "Please do whatever you think best, Doctor," and offered her warm, kind expression.

Thankfully, there was only one other patient in the Suture Room at the time. After numbing the elderly woman's wound, I briefly left her to sew up another patient's leg laceration while the nurse cleaned and prepped Mrs. Hudson's wound. I then returned to her bedside and checked her wound to be sure it remained numb before beginning the wound repair.

It took a good while to close the wound with sutures. The top layer of her elderly skin was like wet Kleenex. If I got too close to the edge of the wound, the suture would simply tear right through the skin.

I had to do a type of closure using dissolvable sutures in a deeper layer that brought the edges of the top layer of skin close together and then used some short "butterfly" bandages to carefully align the skin edges.

All the while I worked on her arm, we carried on a conversation, with me asking her about her childhood and what it was like growing up in her younger years. She was a very pleasant woman who, like many people of that time, faced a lot of challenges and hardships. As I was finishing, I explained to both her and her daughter how to care for the wound as it healed, and asked them to keep an eye out for any evidence of infection, signs of which I described to them.

"Well, in addition to being my best patient of the evening, you also win the prize for the greatest number of stitches thus far tonight—sixteen!" Her response was, "Oh, my! I'm glad we did come to see you, then," followed by her gentle smile. I gave her daughter another wink.

As I stood, I told them I would write down the wound care instructions we talked about so they could refer to them if needed. Both Mrs. Hudson and her daughter expressed their sincere appreciation for the care they had received.

What an enjoyable experience it had been! I couldn't help but think how wonderful it would be if patient care was like that all the time.

As I had put in the last few stitches to Mrs. Hudson's arm, I noticed Avery, our suture-room nurse, bringing in another patient whom she placed in the front right suture bay. I left Mrs. Hudson's bedside and diagonally crossed the room to see our newest patient.

As always, I introduced myself as I approached the stretcher and asked the young man in his midtwenties what had happened to him. He was lying in a prone position on the stretcher, his head on a pillow with his face turned toward me, away from the wall. From my perspective, I could see a bloody area on the back of his head.

"I hit my head on something and it started bleeding," was the reply. No other details were offered. I picked up his chart and made some notes as I went through all the routine questions about other injuries, losing consciousness, meds, allergies, etc., receiving short answers to everything. He was pretty vague about how his injury had actually occurred. He assured me he didn't hit it very hard, later deciding it was the edge of a cabinet that he'd accidentally struck.

Judging from his short and occasionally evasive answers, I figured the patient, who went by Sammy, probably got in a fight with someone. I decided to just anesthetize his wound and explore it, assessing whether there might be any evidence to suggest a skull fracture. I doubted that to be the case, but one should always consider it when the history is vague or inadequate.

I explained the process as I did with all patients who needed sutures. "Any questions before we get started?" I asked. In a somewhat gruff and impatient voice, he asked, "Can you hurry it up? I got to be somewhere." Sammy made no eye contact, having avoided it throughout our brief interaction.

"I'll do the best I can," I answered as I drew up some local anesthetic into the syringe and then changed the needle to the size necessary for injecting his wound.

After numbing him up, I moved to another patient on the back right stretcher who had returned from X-ray with films of his injured left hand. It had some swelling, tenderness, and an abrasion, but no fracture on his X-ray. I explained to him we would clean it up with antiseptic and put on a bulky bandage, which would help reduce the swelling and make him more comfortable. I then stressed the importance of keeping it elevated.

The timing was perfect. Avery had just finished prepping Sammy's wound, so we switched patients. Avery had already laid out all the instruments and the type of suture I had asked for to use in Sammy's wound repair.

Avery had also positioned Sammy closer to the near edge of the stretcher so it would be easier for me to examine and close the wound with sutures. Sammy was still lying in a prone position, but now his face was away from me, toward the wall.

I sat down on a rolling stool and turned on the bright overhead light, adjusting it so the beam focused directly on the laceration. I then put on my sterile gloves and picked up a sterile drape, which was a two-foot-by-two-foot germ-free paper sheet with a three-inch-diameter hole in the center of it.

I explained to Sammy what I was about to do with the sterile drape, emphasizing the importance of him not touching the drape with his hands or it would contaminate the "sterile field" and we would have to stop and get another one.

"Whatever," Sammy said in his not-so-pleasant voice. "Just get it done."

I placed the sterile drape over Sammy's head and face, centering the open hole over the wound. As I began to examine the wound, I could see it was pretty deep, all the way down to his skull. The periosteum, a tough but thin fibrous tissue layer that nourished the bone, was intact. I used my gloved sterile finger to see if I could feel any irregularities in the skull, and did the same using one of the instruments from the tray. No evidence of fracture was present.

"You must have hit your head really hard on that cabinet," I said, knowing that wasn't the real story. "Were you rising up or did you fall into it?" I asked as I was putting the needle with suture into my needle holders.

"Look, Doc, just get it done," was Sammy's reply.

"I'm working on it, Sammy, I just want to be sure we don't miss anything that could cause you problems later."

No response from Sammy.

The wound was shaped somewhat like a Y. It was about an inch and a half long with some swelling around the wound edges. There wasn't much bleeding. The anesthetic used on the scalp helps to temporarily decrease active bleeding. It was clear he got whacked pretty hard.

The great thing about scalp lacerations is that they are usually easy to suture, especially if the laceration is in a pretty straight line. The scalp oftentimes splits along a straight line when it gets rapidly compressed between the hard object striking the scalp and the thick skull beneath it. Other times, one may see the Y-shaped wound like Sammy's—sort of a burst-type wound.

I was putting in the last suture and tying the knot when I noticed someone step through the door of the Suture Room and wave their hand to get my attention.

It was a police officer. When I turned my head toward him, he raised a finger to his lips, instructing me to be quiet.

While I had never yet encountered this type of situation, it didn't actually surprise me. I figured Sammy had gotten his wound from a fight, and it looked like the police had now caught up with him. I guessed they probably were here to arrest him or at least get his side of the story. *Good luck with that,* I thought, reflecting on the fact that Sammy wasn't very conversive.

The police officer kept his finger to his lips with one hand while motioning for me to come toward him with his other hand. I took that to mean he wanted to switch positions.

His sign language suggested I shouldn't divulge his presence, so I continued my conversation. "Sammy, I'm almost finished, I just need to step over and get some antibacterial ointment to go on that cut so it doesn't get infected." I spoke as I scooted the stool back from the stretcher.

"Hurry up, Doc. I'm tired of waiting," was Sammy's reply.

As I walked away from Sammy's stretcher toward the doorway to the Suture Room, the police officer quietly and quickly stepped over to where I had been. To my surprise, three more police officers followed the first into the room, also moving very swiftly and silently.

The lead officer was now standing next to Sammy's left shoulder. He motioned that he would grab Sammy's right arm, and for each of the other officers to grab another one of Sammy's extremities. They nodded their understanding.

When they were all in position, the lead officer mouthed, "Now," and they simultaneously pounced, grabbing each of Sammy's extremities with two hands.

Sammy was completely surprised. The sterile sheet covering his face and head had prevented him from witnessing the entrance and positioning of the police officers. Sammy was about five feet ten, 160 pounds, and had a muscular build. But he was easily overpowered and unable to put up much resistance.

Another officer who had rapidly appeared and followed the other four was now next to Sammy and began hurriedly patting him down as the other officers kept Sammy pinned to the stretcher. He momentarily stopped at Sammy's lower back, subsequently raising up the sweatshirt to reveal a .38-caliber revolver in the waistband of Sammy's pants. The officer carefully retrieved the weapon.

Yikes! I thought. I was glad I hadn't gotten into an argument with Sammy.

As they finished checking for other weapons, they promptly applied handcuffs to Sammy's wrists and then helped him to sit up at the edge of the stretcher. They assisted him in standing and started to lead him away.

I stopped them for a moment so I could put some antibiotic ointment on the wound I had sewn closed and then reached for the discharge instructions for wound care, which they would need for Sammy while he was in jail.

Before leaving, the lead officer thanked me for my assistance. I asked him what had happened since I didn't get much useful information from Sammy about the circumstances related to his wound. I wanted to be sure there wasn't some other potential injury that might require consideration before Sammy's departure.

The officer told me Sammy had gotten into a "verbal disagreement" with the woman with whom he was living. They had two small children between them. One was about eighteen months old, and the other a year older. The kids started crying because of Sammy's shouting. So Sammy walked over to the window, opened it up, and then walked back to the oldest child, picked him up, returned to the window, and threw him out.

Their apartment was on the second floor.

Sammy then went back, grabbed the younger child, and headed back to the window. As he was throwing the second child out, his girlfriend struck him on the back of the head with a frying pan in an effort to stop him.

I envisioned the two small children flying out the window and landing on a concrete parking lot twelve feet below. I grimaced at the thought, imagining they must have been killed or very seriously injured.

The police officer read the expression on my face and said, "Amazingly, each child landed in bushes, which broke their fall. They barely had a scratch on them. They were transported to the nearby children's hospital, but without any apparent injuries."

The officer went on to tell me that Sammy struck his girlfriend in the face after she hit him, knocking her to the floor. He then grabbed his gun and left. Thankfully, he did not shoot her. She dialed 911, reported the incident, and told police Sammy had a gun. They knew he would probably be looking for treatment. His girlfriend said she hit him pretty hard. His head wound certainly bore witness to that.

It's hard to fathom how anyone could do such an unconscionable act against small, defenseless children. Yet, in today's news, we too often hear of even greater tragedies committed against schoolchildren and other defenseless people.

Unfortunately, ER clinicians bear witness to such tragedies. Hatred and violence have become far too much a part of our culture.

Regrettably, we don't hear enough about folks like Mrs. Hudson and her daughter—people who provide examples of how to treat one another and who view their own troubles in the greater context of others.

Sometimes, it seems as though it takes nationwide tribulations and difficulties to help us recognize the plight of others and reach out to support and encourage one another.

As a country, we must move past the polarization, division, and self-centeredness that have become far too prevalent in our nation today. I have no doubt that as a people, and as a nation, we are capable of creating a much better future.

Yikes!

"Line three for you, Dr. Grant. It's an attorney, Gerald Jenkins," Carol, our ER secretary, said as I whisked by the nurses' desk to drop a couple of charts into the "Orders" box. Those last words stopped me in my tracks.

"An attorney?" I asked. "Yes," she said as she smiled, probably amused by how quickly my face lost its color.

I didn't have a personal attorney, so it was likely one of two possibilities—either this was an attorney who wanted to sue me on behalf of a patient I had seen previously, or it was an attorney looking for someone to review a case where another doctor was being sued by a patient they had seen. Neither option was appealing to consider.

Normally, I would have asked the secretary to take a message, but I had to know which this was. Postponing it would just create more anxiety. I headed back to our little "doctor's office," which was essentially a small closet with a connecting bathroom. I picked up the phone sitting on the wooden desk and punched line three.

"This is Dr. Grant," I said in a neutral tone of voice, trying hard not to reveal my anxiety. "Hello, Dr. Grant, this is Gerald Jenkins. I was referred to you by a physician colleague of yours who felt you were qualified to review a medical malpractice case." I tried hard not to audibly utter the giant sigh of relief sweeping through my brain.

I had never reviewed a medical malpractice case as an "expert witness" before and didn't really like the idea of serving in that role. However, one of the faculty physicians in my residency program had encouraged me to do so when I entered private practice.

Working with a lawyer in this setting wasn't something I really wanted to do, but my faculty doc had given me grounds to consider it.

At the time, he told me, "Nowadays, about thirty-five percent of physicians are sued for malpractice. The odds are pretty good that one day you'll be sued. Who would you want to review the case against you—some doc who isn't qualified to review it from a medical perspective and just wants to get paid for his time, or a qualified physician who is board-certified in emergency medicine?"

That thought had stayed with me. When I graduated from my residency program in emergency medicine, I was as naïve as most graduates. I thought that if I just practiced good medicine and tried to take the best care of my patients, I wouldn't need to worry about medical malpractice—that only affected the "bad doctors." In the years to come, I would understand the real truth, probably more so than most.

"Who was the physician who recommended me?" I asked, hoping that information might influence my decision as to whether to get involved in the case. "Dr. Steven Dockins," he said. I knew Steve—he was a very capable and kind physician.

"I've not served as an expert witness before," I said, wanting to be completely transparent. Maybe the attorney would prefer someone who had experience.

"That's not a problem, Doctor," Gerald said. "My understanding is that you have been residency trained in the specialty of emergency medicine, are board-certified, and are well respected in the medical community." The attorney paused briefly and then continued, "If you're willing to review the case for us, I will send the documents to you for your assessment. Basically, this case involves a doctor who examined a small child in the ER who received a scratch to her ear during the examination. The patient's mother is suing the doctor for twenty-five thousand dollars."

My mind raced to consider the many possibilities that might have resulted in such a lawsuit: Perhaps the scratch had later become seriously infected and caused the patient to be on a long course of antibiotics or required some drainage procedure. Or perhaps the scratch was actually an injury to the eardrum, resulting in temporary or permanent hearing loss. Or— I snapped back to the conversation at hand.

"You can send the documents to me at the following post office box," I said and then started to provide the address.

The attorney interrupted me. "Excuse me, Doctor, but if you're OK with it, I will send a courier with the file to the emergency room of your hospital right away."

Wow, I thought, *that's definitely express mail!* Then the cynical part of me thought, *Of course, attorneys can afford to do business that way. Ultimately, their clients pay for it.*

"That will be fine," I said. "I will be here until seven tonight." We said goodbye to each other and I then hurried out to the front desk to see what patients entered the ER during those few minutes I was on the phone. I didn't have time to give the call another thought until I was off shift later that evening.

I finished my charting on the last handful of patients I had seen near the end of my shift. I hated to "turn over" patients to the new doctor coming onto the evening shift. Unless those patients would require a workup that would take more than another hour, I didn't mind staying late to finish up their evaluation, testing, and disposition. Most of the other ER docs in our group did the same.

After I talked to the last patient about their diagnosis and treatment plan before sending them home that night, I headed back to the physician's office to open the packet I had received from the attorney.

It was a pretty thick packet, which I hastily opened. There were pages and pages of information, much more than I had anticipated. Some of the documents I didn't recognize as I scanned the pages for the physician's handwritten note. Finding it, I read his perspective regarding the encounter—basically, the child presented with a history of having fever and "pulling at her ears." That complaint was often associated with an ear infection in young children.

The physician had examined the child thoroughly and looked in her ears. One eardrum was red, reflecting infection, which the doctor diagnosed as such and prescribed antibiotics.

I sifted through all of the other documents, including depositions by both the patient's mother and the doctor, and a couple of nurses. The gist of the case was that as the patient was being discharged, the mother noticed a tiny drop of blood on the child's external ear, the part of the ear one can see on the side of the head.

She told the nurse, who then told the doctor. The doctor came back in and reexamined the child's ear again and saw no blood coming from the ear canal, only noting a tiny scratch on the outside of the ear. There was no continued bleeding.

He asked the nurse to clean it with some disinfectant and put a small drop of antibiotic ointment on it. He explained to the mother that perhaps the scratch happened as they held the child and looked in her ears, but it wouldn't change the child's treatment—it would heal without incident.

Of course, as an ER physician, I also knew it's common for small children with earaches to reach up and scratch their ear because it's bothering them. If one doesn't keep their little fingernails trimmed closely, they can create scrapes that result in minor bleeding.

I looked for documents that might suggest a subsequent infection related to the scratch, or other unlikely but possible conditions I had considered. There weren't any. I was puzzled.

This was it? The doctor was being sued by the patient's mother because of a tiny scratch on the outside of the ear, which may or may not have been related to the exam? And there were no subsequent problems or complications? As a naïve young emergency medicine physician, I felt as though I had just entered the *Twilight Zone.*

On my next day off, I called the attorney to discuss my "expert opinion." I explained that the doctor clearly met the standard of care, and I did not see the tiny scratch as an unusual complication of trying to hold a small, anxious child while examining them. Whether the child had done it herself or whether it happened while trying to examine the ear I could not say.

At some point, I expressed to the attorney my astonishment that this was a lawsuit. There was no inappropriate or reckless care, and there was no significant injury or subsequent required treatment.

That's where my education regarding medical malpractice truly began.

The attorney explained to me that this was, in his opinion, a "nuisance" suit, meaning that the plaintiff's attorney would file the case on behalf of the patient, not expecting it to go to trial, which would be costly for both parties. The hope of the plaintiff's attorney was that the insurance company would do the math and realize it would be more costly to defend the case at a trial, and instead choose to settle for a sum of money less than the cost of a trial. Twenty-five thousand would get negotiated down to about fifteen thousand, a much more reasonable "expense."

The attorney then conveyed that the insurance company defending the physician had recognized this recently growing trend by plaintiff's attorneys who hoped to earn easy money. The insurance company had decided to defend *all* nuisance cases, demonstrating they would no longer provide plaintiff attorneys an incentive to file them. This would result in rising expenses for the plaintiff's attorney as proceedings were drawn out with their risk of winning the case simultaneously dropping, certainly a disincentive for playing this game.

I realized how little I truly understood about medical malpractice. My original impression was completely untrue—that physicians who practice good medicine and care about their patients don't need to worry about being sued for medical malpractice.

A few weeks later, I touched base with the defense attorney again. He let me know that the case had been dropped. Once the plaintiff's attorney realized there wasn't going to be a quick payout, they suggested strongly to their client that the case not be pursued further. Of course, the reality is it should have never been filed.

Having now unwittingly entered the medical-legal world, it didn't take long to be asked again for my "expert medical opinion" on other cases. My faculty mentor had foreseeably alerted me to this possibility. While encouraging me to review one or two cases a year, he suggested I not do more than that.

His concern was that if one served as an "expert" too often, that physician might begin to look like a "hired gun," potentially negating some of their effectiveness as an expert witness.

That sounded reasonable to me, so my maximum involvement was two cases within a year's time frame. With each case, my exposure to the medical-legal world grew. I enjoyed learning about the legal system and how it worked. And I found it helpful to understand and analyze the type of medical cases resulting in litigation.

Another clairvoyant recommendation by my faculty mentor was to carefully review a case without bias—to stay focused on the facts and be objective, developing one's own perspective about the patient visit and the care they received. His reason for this became obvious with his warning that followed—attorneys, whether for the plaintiff or the defendant, would likely try to shape or mold my opinion.

"They may try to rephrase what you've said so that it's more in line with what they are looking for and then ask you if they understood it correctly. Don't let them do it!" my mentor had emphatically said.

"Hold to your analysis and perspective. This is *your* professional opinion. *Do not* let them change it to anything else."

Ultimately, the case is supposed to come down to whether the physician caring for the patient provided what the legal folks refer to as the "standard of care," meaning whether the doctor in the case did what a "reasonable" doctor would do under similar circumstances.

I recognized the wisdom of all the advice and instruction my mentor had provided me. And my knowledge of the system and its nuances and pitfalls continued to grow.

Along the way, I was exposed to a concept that terrified me as a physician. It came from a very knowledgeable and experienced attorney who had asked me to review a very important case.

The litigation was going to trial, and the attorney was asking me questions he might pose at trial. In response to one of his questions, I began to explain the science supporting the appropriate and necessary treatment the physician had provided, clearly demonstrating he had done the right thing.

After carefully listening for several minutes, the attorney said, "Dr. Grant, I'm sure that everything you said was true. I followed most of it, but you must understand something. Most of the people on the jury probably won't grasp some of what you tell them. In fact, some of them won't even try to understand. It simply boils down to this—do they like you? Do they believe you are a sincere, caring doctor?" He paused for a moment to be sure what he said was sinking in.

"That matters more than any medical explanation you provide. If they like you, they will believe you and agree with whatever you tell them, whether they comprehend it or not."

I was stunned into silence. I was dumbfounded. Surely, that was not what this all boiled down to. Surely, the legal decision about whether the medical treatment a doctor provided was based on medical standards and practices, and the science behind it—not just whether the jury liked one "expert" doctor who testified more than another.

I was mortified to think that the outcome of medical malpractice lawsuits wasn't always about doctors who practice "good medicine" versus "bad medicine," but rather attorneys and "experts" who are able to sway juries by means of their personality, and in some cases, their *acting*. Yes, their *acting*. I had already witnessed it from opposing experts who attempted to put forth ludicrous and medically unfounded statements regarding appropriate care. It was unconscionable.

Over the next ten-plus years, as I continued to serve as an expert witness, I firmly concluded the attorney had imparted to me the absolute truth. It was sad, and horribly unfair, to know that one's medical career might be completely destroyed based on which "experts" a jury might find more likable or appealing, rather than the appropriateness of the medical care provided. It was disturbing to think that decisions might not be founded upon the science of medicine and the quality of patient care but rather the performance of the "actors" in front of the jury. Patients with legitimate lawsuits against physicians fell prey to the same injustice.

In the years following that incredible revelation by the attorney, I read with increasing interest various medical malpractice cases reported in the news. At one point, I was stunned to read about a case in which a patient who professed to have supernatural powers asserted that aspects of their medical care and testing subsequently interfered with their ability to use their supernatural powers.

While that claim might cause one to smile at its apparent farcical nature, the patient initially won the case and was awarded more than half a million dollars.

After my initial astonishment subsided regarding the outcome of the case, I supposed the plaintiff's physician expert must have been carefully selected. No doubt he or she was an attractive, compelling, articulate, personable, and very likable witness.

With the size of the award and the unanticipated outcome, I imagined the expert must have also had a great deal of prior experience—acting experience, that is, perhaps even playing the part of a well-respected and admired doctor in a TV series or on the big screen. It appeared the plaintiff's attorney had chosen well in the casting call for the case.

Connecting

To be a good physician, there are many skills one must master. One of the most basic, and important, is communication with the patient. Of course, it sounds easy, but that's not always the case. Sometimes it can actually be the most difficult facet of the patient visit.

From the medical perspective, the key component of patient-physician communication is referred to by clinicians as "taking the patient's history." That simply means gaining a thorough understanding of the main problem or concern for which the patient came to the emergency room.

Again, it seems pretty straightforward—just ask the patient what the problem is and receive the answer. Well, it doesn't always work that way, as Mr. Johnson taught me.

~ ~ ~

"Hello, Mr. Johnson, I'm Dr. Grant," I said as I entered the room and looked across to the elderly man sitting in the chair opposite the door, his old felt hat in his hand. I walked over and extended my hand to him.

Mr. Johnson stood up and shook hands with me.

"Pleased to meet ya, Doctor, suhr." Even if you couldn't see Mr. Johnson, the cadence and tenor of his speech made it readily apparent he was from the Deep South. His voice was a full-bodied baritone, combined with a Southern drawl that was easily distinguishable. And his mannerisms spoke to a custom of politeness and civility—a wonderful yet too infrequent occurrence in today's world.

When he stood up, I saw he was much taller than I had judged while he was seated. He was a muscular, slender gentleman who was in his seventies. He had aged gracefully, as they say, with his hair mostly gray but his other features providing the appearance of a younger man.

"Please be seated, Mr. Johnson," I said after we shook hands.

"Suhr?" he said in his rich resonating voice as he lifted his left hand and cupped it behind his left ear.

"Please be seated," I said again, this time speaking more loudly and motioning toward the chair.

"Yes, suhr, Doctor. Thank ya." His tall frame of about six foot four resumed its sitting position from which it had risen. That was one thing I consistently admired and appreciated about elderly people—they seemed to always be courteous and appreciative of any assistance provided. They invariably addressed you as "Doctor" or "sir" or "ma'am," even if your face was as young and smooth as a baby's behind.

"Now, then, Mr. Johnson, what brings you to the emergency room today?" I asked as I pulled a rolling stool closer to Mr. Johnson's chair, which was about three feet in front of me. I sat down and relaxed as I leaned forward and rested my elbows on my knees. At three o'clock in the morning, it wasn't busy, and I was looking forward to talking with this senior gentleman without being in the usual rush.

"Suhr?" Mr. Johnson asked, once again holding up his left hand to his left ear and leaning toward me while still seated in his chair. I had forgotten to talk louder than normal, asking that last question in my usual tone of voice.

I increased my volume. "I said, 'What brings you to the hospital today, Mr. Johnson?'" This time, I was leaning toward him as I spoke.

The genteel older man smiled and rested both of his large hands, one on top of the other, on the erect walking cane he held between his legs in front of him.

"Well, suhr, I reckon it was my '57 Chevy."

He looked directly at me as he answered, his hands still on his walking cane. The sincerity of his answer and the expression on his face brought a broad smile to mine. He had not intended it as a joke but rather a factual response to my question.

"No, Mr. Johnson, I mean, why did you come to the hospital tonight?" This time, I remembered to talk loudly, but perhaps it hadn't been loud enough.

Mr. Johnson cocked his head to the side and kind of looked at me out of the corner of one eye. I wasn't sure whether he had heard me or whether he just wasn't sure of what I meant by the question. Either way, I got no response except for the inquisitive look.

I increased the volume of my voice further. "Why did you decide to come into the hospital tonight?" Again, I leaned toward Mr. Johnson as I spoke. I then repeated the question: "What was it that made you decide to come to the hospital at three o'clock this morning?"

The gentleman straightened up a little after the question and looked directly toward me, over his crossed hands on the walking stick, smiling again. I felt as though this meant he had comprehended my question and was contemplating his answer, in no hurry to verbalize it.

"Well, suhr, I was drivin' by the hospital when I saw there was an empty parking space out front, so I stopped to come inside." I waited for more as he looked toward me. There was a short pause of silence during which I let the words of his deep harmonious voice just wash over me. His voice was so rich and soothing. After a brief hesitation, he spoke again.

"You know, I've never been by here in the day when there was a parking space, so I thought that since there was one now, I ought to take advantage of it." He spoke all of this completely straight-faced with unmistakable sincerity.

I thought about how often I had tried to get a parking place myself and how he was right about there never being one during the day. Although it wasn't the answer I anticipated, it did make sense. I couldn't help but grin. I could see that taking Mr. Johnson's history would likely entail a longer conversation.

I paused for a moment, trying to think of a way to ask the question in a manner likely to provide the response I was looking for. I looked down at the chart in my hands to see if the nurses had written any additional information that might help me to get us on the same wavelength.

"Blood in the stools," was the chief complaint recorded on Mr. Johnson's chart. That complaint is not unusual in the elderly population, oftentimes related to hemorrhoids. And Mr. Johnson seemed comfortable and in no distress.

I tried again, making sure I kept my volume up, looking him straight in the eyes so he could see the movement of my lips, which sometimes helps those who are hearing impaired.

"Do you have some blood in your stools?" I asked as I leaned over toward him and he leaned a little in my direction.

Mr. Johnson smiled as he straightened up. "No, suhr, Doctor, this chair is just fine!" he said as he put his hands on top of his walking cane again.

I half sighed and half laughed. I was glad it wasn't busy. This was going to take some time.

I momentarily thought—and hoped—I might be able to improve Mr. Johnson's hearing if he suffered from cerumen impaction, a common ailment in older patients with hearing difficulty, although it's not exclusive to that age group. Cerumen impaction is simply a buildup of earwax that eventually fills the ear canal, blocking much of the sound from getting to the eardrums.

If that was the cause of Mr. Johnson's hearing impairment, we could substantially improve it by clearing out the wax.

I needed to take a quick look in his ear canals, but first, I wanted to help him understand what I would be doing. Rather than another verbal exchange at this point, I opted for some "sign language."

I stepped over to the wall and grasped an otoscope, a device used for looking in one's ear canal. Both the otoscope and the ophthalmoscope (used to look inside one's eyes) were hanging in a wall-mounted structure that provided power to the devices through a connected cable.

To the end of the otoscope, I attached a disposable tip, which sort of looks like a very small, skinny funnel. Then I sat down in front of Mr. Johnson and demonstrated putting the tip of the otoscope into one of my ears, after which I took it out and pointed at him.

He smiled and nodded in the affirmative, apparently grasping what I had communicated to him. Progress!

I then stood at Mr. Johnson's left side, bending over as I looked into his left ear canal. Surprisingly, the canal was clean, without any wax buildup at all. His eardrum mostly appeared normal, although it had a diffuse, faint white appearance to it.

That sometimes means it has some scarring and is not as flexible as normal, thereby impeding one's hearing.

I moved around Mr. Johnson to his right side and repeated the process. The appearance of his right canal and drum were the same as in his left ear.

With no cerumen impaction in either ear canal, we had ruled out one cause of hearing impairment, but the appearance of his eardrums suggested they may have decreased responsiveness, which contributed to his diminished hearing.

The hope for a quick and easy solution rapidly faded. We were back to square one, but I was not deterred.

I reached for his medical chart and took one of the sheets of paper out and turned it over so I could write on the back side. Anticipating his eyesight might not be much better than his hearing, I wrote my question in large capital letters: "What can we help you with tonight?" Then I handed him the chart and pointed to the words I had written on the page.

Mr. Johnson leaned his walking cane against the inside of his right leg and took the chart and glanced at the writing. He then looked up at me, smiled again, and said, "Doctor, suhr, I'm afraid I can't read very well, especially without my glasses. I did not think to bring them tonight." His smile persisted as he handed the chart back to me.

Another obstacle! I was starting to feel like I was in a maze, encountering impasse after impasse.

I had another idea. The registration clerk and the nurse had been able to document some information on his chart, much of which they had probably gotten from his driver's license and his Medicare card, but maybe someone had actually come with him and was either in the waiting room or perhaps in the restroom.

I looked at Mr. Johnson, returned his smile, and loudly informed him that I would be right back, attempting to provide gestures in support of my words. He seemed to have understood. He smiled and nodded, gently waved his right hand toward the door, and then returned both hands to his walking cane before him.

I stood up, headed out the door, and went first to the nurse whose name was on the chart. Pam, the nurse, grinned as I approached. "A little hard of hearing, isn't he?" she said as she was restocking supplies on the cart in front of her. I returned her cheerful smile. "Yes, it's pretty challenging."

I asked Pam if anyone had come with Mr. Johnson, to which she replied, "No." I thanked her and was about to leave when she said, "Just FYI, with the necessary increase in volume, the whole ER has heard the story thus far—even with the door shut." Another grin.

I then headed out to the registration desk, asking the same question and receiving the same answer.

With no other patients to be seen at that moment, I slowly walked back to Mr. Johnson's room, trying to come up with some solution for effectively communicating with him. As I approached the room, I remembered a conversation my older brother, Austin, and I had in years past. He is a veterinarian and frequently enjoys telling me how much harder it is to be a veterinarian than a medical doctor.

I recognized it as a continuation of a long-term sibling rivalry, along with his desire to debate the topic. When I inquired why that might be the case, his words now echoed in my ears: "Because my patients can't talk to me and tell me what's wrong." Austin always thought that ended the debate in his favor.

I smiled as I opened the door to Mr. Johnson's room and once again sat down on the stool in front of him. As I pondered what to do next, I looked down toward the floor. It was then that I saw it! The answer was right in front of me—literally right in front of me.

I reached for my stethoscope hanging down from around my neck and motioned to Mr. Johnson that I was going to put it in his ears. He seemed a little confused as to what my intention was. I put the listening ends of the stethoscope into his ears and picked up the diaphragm end of the stethoscope that goes against the patient's skin and raised it to my mouth to speak toward it. He then clearly got the idea.

It was an unusual form of hearing aid, but it allowed us to now have a conversation. I had the opportunity to hear much more of his melodious Southern drawl, and he actually got to hear my voice as well.

As it turned out, the answers to the questions he could now hear helped me determine that he indeed had some hemorrhoids with a little bleeding. His exam confirmed that diagnosis, and we were able to send him home with some medicine for his hemorrhoids and a stool softener to help with a mild degree of constipation.

He used his walking cane as he strolled out of the ER and back to his '57 Chevy. He expressed his sincere appreciation for the care we provided that evening, and gave us all one last broad smile. He seemed satisfied that he had made the best of an empty parking space in front of the emergency room at three o'clock in the morning. And I had enjoyed his company while discovering an approach I could use again in the future.

~ ~ ~

There is truly an art to history taking. It's a skill that all physicians need to master.

In the second year of medical school, one of our teaching physicians told us that a physician can determine the diagnosis for a given patient about 90 percent of the time through the process of "taking a history."

Of course, at the time, with our very limited knowledge and experience in medicine, we almost laughed at that statement regarding the patient history. Certainly, we didn't believe it—thinking it was just hyperbole intended to gain our attention. Looking back, that perspective clearly demonstrated our gross ignorance at the onset of our journey in medicine.

Over the next twenty years of my medical career, I found the statement increasingly valid. Delving more deeply into a patient's symptoms through a series of more defining questions such as the type of symptom onset (sudden versus gradual), duration (seconds, hours, etc.), quality of pain (sharp, dull, cramping, tearing, etc.), modifying factors that might improve or worsen the symptoms, and a host of other refining queries helps the clinician to focus on the most likely diagnoses to consider for a well-defined and distinct pattern of symptoms.

It became clear to me that the teaching physician had been so very accurate in the words he spoke. Clearly, he was a master in the art of history taking.

During those same twenty years, advances in science and technology have provided physicians with many more testing capabilities, some of which are incredibly wonderful in the information they provide.

That plethora of tests that can now be ordered by physicians may also represent a temptation to rely upon test results to make a diagnosis, rather than using the tests to *confirm* or *narrow down* the possible diagnoses suspected from the patient's history and physical examination.

In some ways, ordering tests can be a time-saver for the physician. Rather than investing the time to take a detailed history, he or she can simply write orders for various tests and go see the next patient while others come to draw the blood, take the X-ray, do the heart tracing, etc. Many times, the tests may be interpreted by others with written or verbal results conveyed to the physician seeing the patient.

Unfortunately, that approach doesn't always provide the answer and sometimes may even mislead the physician if a good history was not taken and an appropriate examination was not conducted.

Becoming skilled in the performance of a concise and directed patient history requires substantial experience—there are so many symptoms and so many diseases, not to mention the extensive diversity of people's personalities, perspectives, and physical makeup.

With some folks, one may just ask them what's wrong and they will provide a succinct story and include most of the pertinent facts. For others, one could give them half the day, and they might communicate everything except what caused them to come to the emergency room!

Of course, sometimes one may encounter very challenging communication problems, such as the patient's inability to fluently speak the same language, which make history taking very difficult.

And sometimes the patient and physician may speak the very same language, only the patient is unable to hear it—as with our very amiable and pleasant Mr. Johnson!

Crisis in Room 3

"They need you in there!" Stacey said as she waved her hand at me, standing at the far end of the nurses' desk with the telephone in her other hand. I had been walking down the hallway of the ER toward the parking lot when she flagged me down. I wasn't on shift that day—I had just come into the hospital to pick up some items I needed to teach a class for the paramedics.

I abruptly stopped walking. "What's up?"

Before Stacey could answer, the door to Room 3, the major resuscitation room, swung open right next to me. One of the nurses stepped out of the room while still holding the door handle behind her and partially closing the door.

She forcefully said to Stacey, "Call Dr. Jeffrey and tell him we need him here *stat*!" The urgency in her voice conveyed they must have a critically ill, unstable patient in Room 3 who was at high risk of dying or had already died and they were trying to resuscitate.

"Also, page overhead and ask for any general surgeon to come to the emergency room *stat*!" As soon as she finished speaking, she swiftly disappeared behind the closing door.

The overhead page the nurse had asked for was unusual. Rarely did we page for "any surgeon available in house." That meant that the patient in Room 3 needed *immediate* surgery, which was not a good sign.

While the door had been partially open, I heard multiple doctors' voices, including Dr. William Jackson, who headed up our group of emergency physicians, and Dr. James Tindle, one of the well-respected and competent ENT (ear/nose/throat) surgeons at the hospital. There were a number of other voices, as well, that I could not readily identify.

Dr. Jackson was really good at managing patients and an excellent diagnostician—someone who could rapidly figure out a patient's problem, oftentimes based on their presenting complaints. That was the nice thing about the group of ER physicians I worked with—they were all very well qualified.

Stacey spoke to me as she dialed the next telephone number. "It's a little kid who is not breathing. They need some help!" She placed the page overhead for the surgeon, which immediately came out over the speakers in the ceiling.

If they were looking for another surgeon and the child was not breathing, there was a good chance they would need to perform a tracheotomy—a surgical procedure in which a hole is cut in the front portion of the child's neck to provide an alternate opening for breathing. It can be necessary when something blocks the child's upper airway or throat, preventing the patient from being able to breathe through their nose or mouth. There were a variety of causes that could lead to such a situation.

I stepped toward Room 3 and gently cracked open the door enough to look inside. When a resuscitation is happening, one doesn't want to open the door too far or too suddenly, as it may knock someone over who is hurriedly moving through the room, attempting to carry out tasks as expeditiously as possible.

The room was indeed pulsating with voices and activity. In the center of the room was the stretcher with six or seven people standing around it, all working on a small child. Dr.

Jackson, the ER physician, was standing at the head of the bed, bending over with a laryngoscope in his hand, about to place it in the small child's mouth.

The respiratory therapist was standing next to Dr. Jackson with the suction, waiting to assist him if needed to clear the child's airway of secretions (saliva, mucous, vomitus, etc.). There were two nurses on each side of the child, all looking for a vein to start an IV on the patient.

With no one standing in front of the door, I opened it enough to slip inside. I could see others once I got inside. Two paramedics were standing against the wall near the foot of the stretcher trying to stay out of the way. Both of them were perspiring profusely. I imagined it was because they had been frantically working on the child as they transported her to the hospital in the ambulance.

Dr. Tindle was also standing against the wall adjacent to the door. He was not providing care at the moment but attentively watching the activity.

I could feel the emotion and intensity in the room as soon as I entered. Each person was laser focused on what they could do individually and collectively to help save a small child's life, which appeared to be in jeopardy at that moment.

One of the nurses hurriedly moved back and forth between one of the cabinets and the stretcher, rapidly opening packaging for equipment and medicines.

"IV in place!" the nurse standing on the right side of the stretcher verbalized loudly to all in the room. She continued to work on taping it in place.

"I've still got a pulse, but the rate is slowing." Rosalyn, one of the more experienced nurses, was holding the little girl's arm in her right hand, feeling for a pulse as she looked up at the cardiac monitor mounted over the head of the bed.

Dr. Jackson removed the laryngoscope from the child's mouth and stepped back so the respiratory therapist could use a pediatric-size BVM to try to push oxygen into the child's lungs while Dr. Jackson regrouped. He moved over to the left side of the stretcher.

"What do you have, Dr. J?" I asked, trying not to break his concentration at the wrong time. He looked up at me just long enough to speak briefly.

"I've got an eighteen-month-old brought in by ambulance with a history of not breathing. Mom saw the child choking, but she doesn't know what happened. That's all we know." He looked back toward the child as he put his stethoscope to her chest.

After listening for a moment, he spoke again, this time to the respiratory therapist. "Is she hard to bag?" If she was, then it meant there was resistance to airflow into her lungs.

The respiratory therapist had been desperately trying to get a very good seal around the child's mouth with the mask so that he could effectively get as much oxygen as possible into the child's lungs.

"Very hard," he replied without looking away from the child he was working on.

Dr. Jackson glanced at me. "I think she must have some foreign body in her airway, but I can't see it and I can't visualize her vocal cords to intubate her." There was profuse perspiration across his forehead and in the armpits of his scrubs.

He looked back toward the child and continued to speak. "We're not adequately oxygenating her. If we can't get an airway established quickly, she's not going make it." He moved back toward the head of the stretcher and picked up the laryngoscope again, changing the end of it (referred to as the "blade") to see if a different blade would work better.

Just before he waved the respiratory therapist off to try looking into the child's throat again, he spoke to me once more.

"Would you do a tracheotomy on this child?" he asked as he put the laryngoscope into the child's mouth to look for a foreign body and try again to establish an airway.

Although I didn't say it, the answer in my mind was an immediate *no*! Performing a surgical tracheotomy on a child this age and size was something *no one* wanted to do, not even an experienced ENT surgeon. I had never needed to do one on a child in an emergency situation, and I didn't want to start now. Neither did Dr. Jackson, which was why he was asking me. It appeared that Dr. Tindle did not feel the procedure would have a good outcome, which is why he had not stepped forward earlier.

I moved up next to the stretcher to take a look at the child. It was a sight that would make any physician feel ill. The child's skin color had become a dusky blue, which meant there was not enough oxygen in her bloodstream. She was unconscious, completely limp, and not moving, despite all of the needle sticks and other procedures she had endured—another very bad sign.

She did, however, try to take a tiny breath. There was no sound, just the slightest movement of her abdomen as her diaphragm muscle pulled down at the bottom of the lungs, making her tummy pooch out a little. She was so small.

"Shoot!" Dr. Jackson said in frustration as he removed the laryngoscope. "I can't see any landmarks." He looked back to the respiratory therapist. "Keep trying to bag her as best you can."

Suddenly, the door opened, and one of the general surgeons, Dr. Jeffrey, came running into the room. He, too, was perspiring. From the rate of his breathing, he must have run down from upstairs.

"What do you have?" he asked Dr. Jackson in gasping breaths. Will gave him the same story he had provided to me.

"There's no way I could do a tracheotomy on a kid this size," Dr. Jeffrey said. "I'd probably kill her." He looked first at Dr. Jackson and then at Dr. Tindle as if expecting confirmation from them. Technically, it is a very difficult procedure, especially on a child this small, and complications could indeed be disastrous.

Dr. Jackson looked back to me. "You want to try to intubate her?" he asked.

"Sure," I responded, knowing there were no other alternatives and the child would die unless there was a successful intervention. I reached out to take the laryngoscope from Dr. Jackson. I knew that if he was having difficulty, it would be very challenging for me. Still, I wasn't sure why he couldn't see the landmarks in the child's throat—landmarks that tell one where the child's voice box (larynx) and windpipe (trachea) are, as well as the position of the child's esophagus. Landmarks are essential when attempting to place a small tube into the child's trachea.

I quickly moved to the head of the bed and knelt down on the floor, a position that allowed me to be closer to the little girl's face while also providing me with the best angle for looking into her throat. The respiratory therapist took the mask of the BVM away, and I put the laryngoscope blade into the child's mouth.

The laryngoscope instrument is shaped like an L when held in one's hand. The handle grip is the upper part of the L, with the lower, horizontal part of the L (referred to as the blade, although not sharp) being placed into the patient's mouth. There is a small light on the end of the blade that illuminates the patient's mouth as one attempts to look deep into the throat toward the voice box. That opening between the vocal cords leads down to the windpipe, which connects to the lungs.

After suctioning out the secretions in the child's mouth, I hurriedly looked around the inside of her throat. I could now see what Dr. Jackson was talking about. The light was bright in this very small mouth where everything was pinkish red in color and seemed distorted. The normal landmarks one sees when looking deep into the back of someone's throat were not there. I couldn't get oriented.

I swiftly brought the laryngoscope out. I didn't want to spend more than a few seconds looking so we could keep the patient on oxygen as much as possible, which can't be done if the laryngoscope blade is in her mouth.

After I removed the laryngoscope, the respiratory therapist began to bag the patient with oxygen again.

Without looking up, I let the respiratory therapist try to push several more breaths into her lungs before I tried again. In those waiting moments, I continued to look down at the child, noticing how dark and straight her hair was and how smooth her skin appeared. Her face wasn't quite as dusky appearing as the rest of her body. The thought of her dying pressed into the front of my mind. I allowed it to linger for only a split second before pushing it out. I had to do all I could to prevent that from happening.

I couldn't understand why there were no landmarks visible. I wondered if the child had some congenital abnormality that made her anatomy different than other children. Or did she have some strange and unusual disease that precipitated this situation?

In an instant, I mentally flashed through all the anatomy pictures stored in my brain, yet it still didn't make sense. I decided to try another approach, one I had read about but never personally used.

I waved off the therapist and opened the child's mouth to put the laryngoscope blade back in. This time, instead of lifting the tongue with the blade like one usually does, I put the laryngoscope blade further toward the back of the throat and down toward the esophagus, which lies on the back side of the trachea—the structure I had been looking for but couldn't find.

I thought that if I could locate the esophagus for certain, then I would at least have some orientation. As I got the blade, or lower part of the L, into position, I lifted upward, raising the surrounding structures. Once again, all I could see were red-colored mucous membranes in the bright light of the laryngoscope. It all looked the same.

It was like being in a heavy snowstorm where the snow-covered ground, the sky, and everything around you is all completely white—no structure or definition visible, only one continuous, homogeneous color. It's disorienting.

I knew I had to be in the esophagus, however, because of where I had inserted the blade. I put the blade in a little farther and lifted up again, after which I planned to slowly move the laryngoscope backward out of the mouth. At some point, the tip of the blade would meet the junction between the esophagus and the trachea, and near that location, I should be able to see the vocal cords. It was an approach I had never had to use but hoped would work.

As I lifted up on the laryngoscope after repositioning it, I suddenly saw this blob of red material rapidly moving toward me, just beneath the laryngoscope blade. Like an oncoming train, it raced in my direction, then jettisoned out of the child's esophagus, into the back of the child's mouth, and then straight up into the air.

At that moment in time, everything seemed to shift into super-slow motion. I watched as I saw a round red object rise about two inches above the child's mouth, stay suspended there for a moment, and then fall back toward the stretcher just to the right of the child's ear. It bounced once on the stretcher and then down to the floor. It then continued to bounce as it headed toward a corner of the room, just like you would expect a red rubber ball to do when bounced on the floor!

Except for the slight noise made by the bouncing ball, the room was completely frozen in silence. Everyone seemed paralyzed. It was as though they had just seen some alien creature jump up out of this girl's throat and scurry across the room. No one moved.

The brief silence was then broken by a soft, faint cry. In only a few moments, it would become a loud, strong wail. In those seconds, the child's color pinked up swiftly and she began to move around. Within just a few minutes, she would be sitting up wanting her mommy.

Dr. Jackson looked over at me from across the room as I remained on one knee at the head of the stretcher, the laryngoscope in my left hand, my brain still trying to fully process what I had just witnessed.

He was the first to break free of the trance everyone had fallen into as our minds tried to grasp what we had seen.

"Great work, Tom!" Dr. Jackson said, his face beaming with a big grin on it.

I smiled as I looked back at him. I could not help but think to myself, *Luck is definitely better than skill some days!*

In that brief instant between the appearance of the red bouncing ball and the soft cry of the child, it had all made perfect sense. The little girl had put a three-fourths-inch-diameter red rubber ball into her small mouth, and because of its large size relative to her mouth, she had reflexively tried to swallow it. Since it was so big, it had gotten stuck in her esophagus, which pushed against the back of her windpipe. In children of that age, the windpipe is soft and flexible, and can be squeezed shut. The ball closed off her airway, preventing us from being able to easily push air into her lungs with the BVM. And it also distorted the structures of her airway, making it hard to identify the usual landmarks. Inserting the laryngoscope blade into her esophagus and lifting up with it had opened a path for the ball's exit. In retrospect, the tracheotomy would have been of no benefit in this situation and would likely have done much more harm than good.

There is no more wonderful feeling than helping a child so close to death regain the precious yet frail fullness of life.

After reuniting mother and daughter, the child was admitted to the hospital for overnight observation. Amazingly, she went home the next day without any obvious or measurable ill effects.

It's incredible to witness the resiliency of little children. The power of the body's design to fuel continued growth and development, overcoming temporary setbacks and impediments, is amazing. We are incredibly and uniquely designed with capabilities and qualities that only a Master Designer could have envisioned and incorporated into the molecular blueprint of our DNA.

~ ~ ~

When our first child became old enough to eat grapes, my wife put them in a small bowl and placed them on the table in front of our son. Just as he was reaching for one, I snatched up the bowl and headed to the kitchen counter where I began cutting all the grapes into halves or quarters.

I'm sure my wife and son thought Daddy had lost it. When placed back on the table, the grapes no longer looked like cute, tiny pale-green balloons. They also didn't offer that pleasing sensation of feeling one pop in one's mouth when biting down on it.

At the time, I explained to my (nonmedical) wife that, for children our son's age, a full grape could possibly get stuck in their small throat and cut off their airway, precipitating a life-threatening crisis.

That was just one of the many precautions my wife and kiddos had to endure as we grew up together as a family. Thankfully, they all learned to roll with it, usually just chalking it up to Dad's idiosyncrasies (and paranoia)!

GSW

We needed to quickly visualize Ms. Butler's back to look for any bullet wounds. She had come in via EMS on a backboard, which now lay on top of the ER stretcher.

"Let's log roll her onto her right side," I said loudly so all could hear over the background noise from the many activities around me. Trauma Room 1 was filled with EMTs, paramedics, nurses, technicians, and our critically ill patient, Ms. Butler.

Logrolling a patient is a method used to turn a patient onto their side while attempting to maintain alignment of the spine. The approach is used on trauma patients who may have a spinal injury.

The paramedic standing at the head of the stretcher placed his open hands onto each of her shoulders, cradling between his forearms her head and the cervical collar around her neck. This would help keep her head aligned with the rest of her body as we simultaneously rolled her onto her side facing me. I leaned over her body to examine her back.

A large amount of blood had pooled on her back side next to the backboard and clotted, creating a layer of sticky, gelatinous deep-red material that now covered her back. I rapidly wiped away as much as I could, using handfuls of gauze sponges.

"I've got a bullet wound just to the right of her spine at about the T8 to T9 level," I said as I hastily taped a partially straightened paper clip next to the wound, with the straight end pointing to the bloody hole in her back. That marker would show up on the X-ray to help identify where the bullet entered her torso.

The wound location—a few inches below the right shoulder blade—strongly suggested the bullet had gone through a portion of her lung and possibly part of her spine as well. The appearance of the wound indicated the bullet entered at that location. It was about three-eighths of an inch in diameter with relatively smooth edges. Exit wounds are usually larger and more ragged around the periphery.

"OK, I don't see any other wounds," I said as I scanned her back, including her shoulders, buttocks, and upper legs, searching for other visible injuries.

I only had moments to look. Ms. Butler had a very faint carotid pulse with no discernable blood pressure upon her arrival to the ER. If she was to have any chance of survival, we would need to accomplish much in very little time. Quickly identifying, prioritizing, and treating all serious injuries was essential to holding on to the slim possibility of saving her life.

"OK, let's roll her back," I said. We once again attempted to collectively and simultaneously maintain the alignment of her spine as we turned her.

She now lay flat on her back, faceup, an empty look in her open eyes—one that suggested death may have already claimed her. She remained motionless on the six-foot-long ambulance backboard that had multiple handholds running along each of its sides. Her clothes had been cut off in the ambulance in an effort to rapidly identify and address all of her injuries. They had reported finding two gunshot wounds.

Before we initially logrolled her, I had identified an exit wound just to the right of her left breast. The bullet that entered her back appeared to have gone completely through her torso, causing the wound on the front of her chest.

"Give me two more lines," I said as I rapidly but methodically continued her physical exam, knowing that the gunshot wounds were not all that I was looking for. She could have fallen after she was shot and sustained other injuries, or she may have been beaten or stabbed before she was shot. I had to move quickly. I needed to know the full extent of her injuries.

"Make sure they both have blood-transfusion setups," I said in reference to the additional IV lines that were in the process of being started. As I spoke, I mentally registered the location of the second bullet wound. It was in her left, front, upper thigh. It had entered there, but no exit wound was visible. There was no blood coming from it now, perhaps because Ms. Butler had already lost much of her blood from the injuries.

Having checked her torso and extremities, I returned to her face and head where I had started the exam earlier after intubating her airway with a tube immediately upon her arrival. The procedure protected her airway and made it easier for us to breathe for her, which she was unable to adequately do on her own. The respiratory therapist was using a BVM filled with oxygen to squeeze oxygen-rich air into her lungs at a rate of about twenty times a minute.

The layer of pooled blood that had accumulated on her back side also extended into her shoulder-length hair, creating a thick, matted, congealed mass. It was not possible to see any wounds, so I felt with my gloved hands, attempting to identify any breaks in the skin or fractures in the skull or facial bones. There were no palpable fractures, but I noted a shallow, linear, two-inch depression at the back left side of her scalp. The edges were indistinct, suggesting it was not caused by a sharp object or the edge of something hard.

With her exam now completed, I reassessed Ms. Butler's status at this point in the resuscitation. It had been about ten minutes since her arrival in Trauma Room 1. In that brief time, we had received a concise verbal report from EMS on Ms. Butler's condition and treatment before and during transport; placed her on cardiac, BP, and oxygen monitoring devices; secured her airway by placing the tube into her windpipe and initiated manual ventilation with oxygen; established four IV lines—three in her upper extremities and one in her uninjured lower extremity; drawn blood for laboratory tests and for typing and crossing her for blood transfusions; and swiftly but thoroughly examined her in an effort to identify all serious injuries.

Two liters of IV fluids had hurriedly been infused into her veins, and universal-donor blood had just arrived from the laboratory and was being set up for rapid transfusion.

It had been excellent teamwork by all. Yet, Ms. Butler still had no measurable blood pressure.

During EMS transport and upon arrival at the ER, her heart rate had been rapid. On the monitor above the stretcher, her heart rate now began to slow, suggesting the possibility that her body was not getting the oxygen it needed. Most likely, that was due to the lack of adequate blood volume and blood pressure to carry oxygen to her organs, including her heart.

Earlier, I had noted decreased breath sounds in her left chest with dullness to percussion suggesting substantial blood had accumulated there. That blood loss would be in addition to all that was visible on her body, the backboard, and the stretcher. The blood in her chest cavity was also impairing the ability of her left lung to oxygenate any blood that flowed through it.

Bullets often do not travel in a straight path from the entrance wound to the exit wound. However, in this case, it seemed almost certain that the bullet had entered her chest from behind and injured a large blood vessel or her heart, resulting in significant blood loss into the left side of her chest.

I felt again for her carotid pulse.

"She's lost her pulse," I said loudly to the team.

I decided we had no time for X-rays or additional tests. If she had any chance for life, her chest needed to be surgically opened without delay to identify her internal injuries and attempt to stop the bleeding. As I reached for a pair of sterile gloves, I asked the nurses to set up the emergency thoracotomy tray, which contains the necessary instruments to cut open a patient's chest in rapid fashion.

At that same moment, Dr. James Wilson, a general surgeon on call to the ER, came through the door of the trauma room. I had the ER secretary page him earlier when we first received the radio call from the field. At that time, Ms. Butler had a barely perceptible pulse in her neck, which we had just lost.

I hurriedly briefed Dr. Wilson on what he saw before him. "Thirty-year-old female with a small-caliber gunshot wound just to the right of the spine at about T8 or T9 with an exit wound anteriorly, just right of her left breast. Also, an entrance wound to the left upper thigh with no exit wound, and without a large hematoma."

"We have almost three liters of fluid already in her and three units of O negative blood hanging now." I looked up and turned toward him.

"And we just lost her carotid pulse." I began putting on the sterile gloves as I continued speaking to Dr. Wilson. "I was preparing to open her chest, but now that you're here, I'll defer to you."

Surgeons, of course, routinely perform operations in the more stable and structured environment of the operating room. Emergency medicine physicians, on the other hand, are much less frequently called upon to carry out critical surgical interventions in the ER.

Dr. Wilson, the surgeon at the bedside with me, was a quiet man of about fifty. Technically, he was a very skilled surgeon with a slow-but-sure, methodical approach.

"Don't you think we should put in a chest tube first?" he asked, without putting on sterile gloves—a signal to me that he wasn't sure we should proceed in such a rapid fashion.

His question was certainly reasonable—probably one I would have asked myself if I had just walked into this setting without the prior experience of all that had occurred up to this point. However, any additional delay might cost Ms. Butler her only hope for life.

I looked at Dr. Wilson as I conveyed my concern. "If she has lost her pulse due to pericardial tamponade or continued bleeding from internal chest wounds, she'll quickly be beyond our ability to bring her back."

"We need to open her now," I added as Dr. Wilson stood next to me, looking at the young woman, but not yet in motion. I understood his hesitancy.

"You can do it or I will." I picked up the scalpel.

"OK," he said, moving closer to the woman's left side and speaking to one of the nurses. "Give me a pair of sterile gloves."

Just as he spoke, Dr. Greg Morgan, the thoracic surgeon, rushed into the room. I had paged him earlier at the same time

I had paged the general surgeon, not knowing who might be able to respond the quickest to the ER.

"What do we have, Tom?" he asked as he rapidly started rolling up both of his sleeves. Just from the scene before him, he knew that time wasn't an element working in this woman's favor.

I gave him the same brief report I had given Dr. Wilson as Dr. Morgan hastily put on sterile gloves and moved in next to me on the patient's left side. Dr. Wilson had already moved down to the foot of the stretcher, leaving the patient to Greg and me. I finished prepping the woman's chest, having swiftly wiped down the front and left side of her chest with an antiseptic solution as Greg picked up the scalpel.

Thoracic surgeons open up people's chests all the time. They do cardiac bypass surgery and other types of surgery in which they work on organs inside the chest cavity. Greg's well-recognized skill and expertise were readily evident. He made an initial long, linear incision through her skin and intercostal muscles, working down to the lining of Ms. Butler's chest cavity in less than a minute.

His follow-on incision now entered the chest cavity, where a large volume of blood suddenly gushed out. It was as if someone had turned over a bucket of fluid, pouring it out all at once. The blood spilled over the edge of the stretcher and onto the floor.

A rib spreader was promptly inserted between two of Ms. Butler's ribs, and with a cranking mechanism, the two arms of the device spread apart so that the side of the chest wall was pried open, allowing one to now see and access the organs inside.

A nurse hurriedly adjusted the overhead lights, providing needed illumination to the interior of Ms. Butler's chest. Using a suction device, I began to remove the quart or two of blood that filled the back portion of Ms. Butler's chest cavity, allowing us to better identify the source of bleeding.

In the meantime, Greg reached into the pool of blood and felt for Ms. Butler's heart.

"No holes in the heart. It's intact, but inadequately filled."

Miraculously, the bullet had somehow missed the heart even though it appeared to have been in the bullet's path. Greg was able to grossly assess the amount of blood in Ms. Butler's blood vessels by feeling how distended or full her heart was. Despite what had already been administered, she still needed additional blood to replace what she had lost, and was continuing to lose.

As the pool of blood in the chest cavity began to recede, filling suction canisters on the wall with blood, the hilum, or portion of the lung that connects it to the center of the chest became visible. Blood mixed with IV fluids was pouring from several holes in large blood vessels in that area. This was clearly the main source of bleeding.

Again, Greg's expertise was evident. He quickly took a large clamp from the tray and put it across the hilum of the left lung, squeezing closed all of the damaged and bleeding vessels that went to the left lung. The clamp also closed off the tubular airway that led to the left lung. In that brief moment, I knew I would have hesitated to take such an approach, making me all the more thankful for his presence.

He must have read my thoughts. He spoke as he continued to work rapidly, "She can live off one lung if we can stop the bleeding, but she won't make it if we don't get the bleeding stopped fast."

The suction catheters had now cleared the left chest cavity of almost all the blood. The decision to use the large clamp on the hilum had made the difference. But at this point, the heart was not physically beating, or contracting on its own. From the moment Greg had first opened her chest, he had begun massaging the heart, trying to pump whatever blood was left in Ms. Butler's vascular system to the rest of her body. With the primary source of blood loss now contained, the blood transfusions and IV fluids would start filling up her vessels and transporting additional oxygen and nutrients to her organs.

Now, however, we needed to get her heart to start working on its own.

I glanced at the cardiac monitor above the bed. It showed a flat line with only a rare, aberrant electrical impulse. Greg saw the same rhythm.

"Let's give her some intracardiac epinephrine," he said to the nurse standing on the other side of the stretcher from us. She hurriedly reached into the medicine cabinet behind her and brought out the prefilled syringe, handing it to me.

I took the syringe, which has a long skinny needle on it, and after Greg removed his hand from the heart, I inserted the needle directly into Ms. Butler's heart, being careful to avoid the coronary arteries that were on the outer aspect of the heart. I injected the epinephrine (adrenaline) into one of the heart chambers, hoping it would stimulate the heart.

It did not work immediately, but as Greg continued to massage the heart, within a minute, it began to visibly quiver.

"I'll need the internal defibrillators," he calmly said, recognizing the patient was now in coarse ventricular fibrillation—an ineffective heart activity that is unable to pump blood to the rest of the body. However, this type of abnormal heart rhythm might respond to electrical stimulation. He continued to manually squeeze the heart at a rate of about eighty times a minute, doing the job that the normal heart muscle does thousands of times each day.

The nurse handed the internal defibrillators to Greg when they were charged. They have the appearance of two long skinny black rods with a flat circular surface at the far end of each rod. On the other end of the rods are handles connected to electrical cables that go to the defibrillator.

Greg looked up at the cardiac monitor above Ms. Butler to see what effect the defibrillation would have on her heart muscle. The first shock had no impact. Ventricular fibrillation persisted.

"Increase the joules to ten please," he said as he once again positioned each of the paddles on opposite sides of the heart. "Let's give it another try," he remarked as his eyes fixed on the cardiac monitor.

After the shock, the cardiac monitor now showed asystole, or flat line. That meant the heart was generating no electrical activity of its own. Once again, we went through the process of administering the intracardiac adrenaline to see if it would have any effect. Once again, the heart began to quiver slightly, and Greg internally defibrillated the heart muscle. Once again, asystole returned.

We repeated this process several more times, but we could not reestablish a heart rhythm. Eventually, even the epinephrine failed to have any effect. There was no visible fibrillation of the heart muscle and no electrical impulses visible on the heart monitor. Ms. Butler was now deceased and beyond our ability to resuscitate. There was nothing else that could be done. Despite all of the extraordinary measures, we had failed to bring her back.

The remarkably efficient teamwork had provided Ms. Butler with every possible chance of survival. That knowledge, however, was little comfort to those who had done their best to save her life. The room was filled with disappointment. Accepting the finality of death in these circumstances was difficult and heartbreaking.

I interrupted the distressing silence in the room. "Excellent teamwork," I said as I glanced around the room looking into the eyes of all who had given their best. "We did everything possible to save her life. It was just too late. She had lost too much blood for her body to recover, despite all that we did." I saw a few nods on solemn faces as the loss weighed upon everyone in the room.

I thanked Dr. Wilson and Dr. Morgan for their quick responses to the ER and their efforts to save Ms. Butler's life. I told the EMS crew their rapid actions had given Ms. Butler a chance to live. We just couldn't stop the bleeding and replace the blood fast enough for her to survive.

Recognizing I could offer no more help to Ms. Butler or the resuscitation team, my focus immediately shifted to the other patients in the ER waiting to be seen. I exited the room with Dr. Morgan and Dr. Wilson and glanced at the hallways and chart rack to get a sense of how far behind I might be.

As I closed the door behind me, one of the police officers in the hallway stepped forward to pull me aside and ask about Ms. Butler's status. After letting him know she did not survive, he informed me of the circumstances that caused her injuries.

"She was shot by her fiancé," the police officer began. "A few days ago, she had turned him in, discovering he had physically abused her young daughter from a previous marriage." That information added greater disappointment to our failure to save Ms. Butler. Now a suffering child was without her mother.

Unfortunately, there was more tragedy to the story. "When they arrested the man for the alleged child abuse, he made threats he would come back and kill her. Somehow, he made the $60,000 bail and got out of jail. Despite their efforts to contact Ms. Butler, they had been unable to let her know he had made bail." The police officer looked to the floor and shook his head in disappointment as he related that last statement.

He then looked up at me. It was as if sharing the disturbing information might somehow alleviate some of the terrible anguish he clearly felt.

"He went to her friend's house, where he kicked in the front door and found both of them in the living room. The friend was closest to him, so he immediately shot her in the face, knocking her to the floor. He then shot his fiancée in her leg as she stood up from a chair on the other side of the room. She turned and tried to hobble away toward the back of the house, at which time, he then shot her in the back, knocking her to the floor."

I could see tears starting to pool in the eyes of the police officer. It was hard to comprehend how anyone could do what Ms. Butler's fiancé had done. And his viciousness was not yet finished.

"Then he walked toward her as she tried to crawl away. Once he reached her, he shot her in the head, and then left, apparently convinced he had killed them both."

The details were sickening. It was hard to imagine how anyone could have so much hatred and cruelty.

The information the police officer related had come from Ms. Butler's injured friend. She had been unable to move immediately after being shot in the face and falling to the floor.

Apparently, the fiancé thought she was dead or dying so he turned his attention to his unfortunate fiancée.

The friend had seen it all while lying on the floor, unable to get up or to even try to stem the flow of blood oozing from her own facial wound. That temporary immobility probably saved her life.

An EMS ambulance had transported the friend to another hospital, where she was conscious and able to carry on a conversation. The bullet had shattered her cheekbone but did not penetrate the skull, which had protected her brain. The wound produced enough bleeding, however, to make the shooter think he had killed her. Instead, she had provided information to the police that helped lead to his arrest.

I thanked the officer for letting me know what had happened and reentered Trauma Room 1, needing to momentarily escape further interaction. I closed the door behind me, wincing as I recalled the officer's words. The depth of evil and malice that led to Ms. Butler's death was hard to fathom. It was nauseating.

My mind then shifted to Ms. Butler's exam, perhaps in a subconscious effort to escape the emotion and retreat to objectivity. In my exam, I had not discovered a bullet wound to Ms. Butler's head, only a shallow linear depression in her scalp. I wondered if the officer had received incorrect information. Or might the fiancé actually have missed with his last shot as he hurried to end his fiancée's life? Or did I fail to discover the wound on my examination? With the blood-soaked, tangled hair, it was certainly a possibility.

If a bullet had entered Ms. Butler's skull, the injury to her brain would have likely made our efforts to save her all the more futile. It would have made our failure slightly less painful, knowing that her survival was even more improbable.

But that type of injury seemed inconsistent with Ms. Butler's course in the ER.

As the nurse and technician in the room continued the preparation of Ms. Butler's body for transportation to the medical examiner, I felt a strong need to answer the question.

I once again put on gloves and approached the stretcher on which she lay. I positioned the overhead lights to improve my visibility and used some saline solution to wash away blood and better examine the only potential head wound I had found when searching for injuries. I now had the benefit of time I didn't have before.

With the light and the cleansing saline, it became clear that the linear depression I had initially felt was actually the tract of a bullet. But it had only grazed her scalp, creating a one-and-a-half-inch-long, moderately deep furrow in the skin without penetrating the skull or entering her brain. There were no other head wounds.

Although the significant bleeding from the scalp wound was a lesser contributor to her death, I realized it may have also provided Ms. Butler with a slim possibility to survive the wrath of her fiancé. It seemed likely that Ms. Butler's concussion from the gunshot to her head may have rendered her temporarily immobile also. That, along with the bleeding from the wound, could have caused her fiancé to believe he had killed her.

His walking away at that point gave Ms. Butler a small chance for life. If only there had been more time to reach her and initiate definitive treatment sooner.

I took off my gloves and leaned against the wall with folded arms. I thought about all the circumstances that had aligned to potentially save Ms. Butler from the tragedy she had suffered—the false belief by her fiancé that he had killed her at the scene, the wise decision to "load and go" by the paramedics, the pre-alert by EMS in route to the hospital, the exceptional and efficient teamwork upon Ms. Butler's arrival in the ER, the rapid initiation of blood transfusions, the quick response by the perfect surgeon to address her devastating chest wound, and the fact that a bullet had not damaged her heart or her brain.

Everything seemed to have been in place to reverse the evil inflicted upon her by her fiancé. And yet she still had died. Time had been the one factor that had not aligned in her favor. I anguished over the thought that perhaps only ten more minutes of time could have made the difference between her life and her death.

I felt a tremendous emptiness and hopelessness. I wanted to escape from all that I had seen and heard. I didn't want to be in this place, bearing witness to such incomprehensible depravity.

I was drained of my desire to go see other patients in the ER—to address their illnesses and injuries, which would likely seem insignificant when juxtaposed with this tragedy. It just didn't seem right to leave this young woman without further mourning her ill-fated and heartbreaking death.

Suddenly, the door to Trauma Room 1 opened.

"Dr. Grant, we need you in Room 12 for a really tight asthmatic!" The nurse delivering the message quickly disappeared, closing the door behind her. She knew I would immediately follow. Tight asthmatics can rapidly decompensate, and sometimes abruptly stop breathing.

I would have to temporarily leave the emptiness and the anguish I felt for Ms. Butler in the room with her.

I hurried off to see the next patient.

Listen Carefully

It appeared as though it was raining outside. His shirt was soaking wet, and drops—not beads—of perspiration covered his face. Clearly, Mr. Browning was a very ill man.

"I'm putting some oxygen on you now, Mr. Browning," Carrie said as she gently placed the nasal prongs into his nostrils. Nurses and technicians in the room rapidly carried out their respective activities, knowing that Mr. Browning might "crash" at any moment. His ashen appearance, profuse sweating, and quiet demeanor attested to his critical condition.

"Mr. Browning, my name is Dr. Grant. I know you're not feeling very well, but we are going to see if we can change that." I watched the cardiac monitor above the stretcher as I introduced myself, making sure that Mr. Browning's heart rhythm remained stable while I talked to him about his symptoms.

I asked a series of brief questions as the nurses started an IV, drew blood for lab tests, took vital signs, prepared to do a 12-lead EKG or "heart tracing," and performed other tasks. Mr. Browning's answers to my questions quickly made it apparent he was in the process of having a heart attack. As soon as the 12-lead EKG began printing out on the machine, it was confirmed.

I conveyed to Mr. Browning his diagnosis and that heart attacks are often caused by a blockage in one of the blood vessels that provide oxygenated blood to the heart. We would be doing multiple things simultaneously in an effort to enhance the delivery of oxygen to his heart, which should improve his symptoms of chest pain, difficulty breathing, and sweating.

I also explained to him that we would be watching his heart rhythm closely on the monitor for any signs of irregular heartbeats that might need to be treated.

In medicine, we assess pain over time by asking the patient to assign a number to it, typically on a scale of one to ten, with ten being the worst pain one has ever experienced. Mr. Browning's chest pain began as a ten for him, and had decreased some with the nitroglycerin tablet we had initially given him shortly after his arrival. But that medication had not completely resolved his chest pain. And his blood pressure remained persistently high.

It was time to try a different drug. In the coming years, patients like Mr. Browning would rapidly be whisked away to the cardiac cath lab for angiography and stent placement, but Mr. Browning's visit was before clinical medicine in community hospitals had progressed that far. Treatment in the late '80s and early '90s was still focused on the administration of medications to diminish the workload of the heart and, at times, to try to dissolve the clot obstructing blood flow to the heart.

"Mr. Browning, I'm going to now give you a different type of medicine than what we gave you a few minutes ago. It, too, will help relieve your chest pain." Mr. Browning nodded his head in an affirmative fashion as he quietly leaned back against the upper portion of the stretcher, which had been raised to make him more comfortable.

He was in his midforties, younger than the average heart-attack patient, but he had several significant risk factors for heart disease. One of his parents had a heart attack at an earlier age, and unfortunately, Mr. Browning was also a two-pack-per-day smoker. He carried an extra forty to fifty pounds of weight, which was evident by the adipose tissue hanging over his belt as he lay on the stretcher with his shirt completely open, the heart monitor leads attached to his chest. He continued to perspire, although not quite as profusely as when he had first come in.

"This pill we are about to give you works differently than the other one." I stood next to the stretcher as I talked to him, intermittently looking at the heart monitor above his bed to watch for any irregular heartbeats.

Certain abnormal heartbeats can portend, or precipitate an "arrest" of the heart in which there is a sudden loss of organized electrical activity, preventing it from effectively pumping blood. The term "cardiac arrest" means that one's heart has stopped working and if not addressed quickly and successfully, the patient will die. Or, perhaps, the more accurate statement is that the patient will *remain* dead.

I moved closer to Mr. Browning as the nurse brought me the medicine, which was in the form of a capsule, about the size of a big antibiotic or herbal supplement. I took a large bore needle in one hand and carefully poked a hole in the end of the capsule as I started to explain to him what I needed him to do.

"I want you to put this capsule between your back teeth and then bite down on it for me. There is a hole in it, and when you bite down, you'll feel some liquid gel squirt out of the capsule. That's the medicine." Once again, he nodded his head in affirmation. "Taking it this way will help the medicine work faster," I said as I put it into his mouth.

I reminded him once again after putting the capsule in his mouth, "Be sure to bite down on it and don't swallow it. Just let the gel that comes out of the capsule remain in your mouth where it can be absorbed more readily."

Almost as soon as those words crossed my lips, I noticed a sudden change in Mr. Browning's heart rhythm on the monitor above the bed. I knew it wasn't from the medicine because he hadn't even had time to bite down on the capsule, much less absorb it.

The rhythm on the cardiac monitor was one that precipitated death. It meant that Mr. Browning's heart was now just quivering in his chest, a condition known as ventricular fibrillation.

"Lay him flat!" I exclaimed as I hurriedly reached for the cardiac defibrillator paddles on a stand next to the wall at the head of the bed, strategically placed there for just this type of situation. I hit the charge button that rapidly powered up the device so we could deliver a substantial electrical charge across his chest wall and heart muscle, hopefully reestablishing the normal heart rhythm and restoring blood flow to Mr. Browning's body.

Carrie, the nurse standing on the other side of the stretcher, had instantly released the lock on the upper portion of the stretcher and laid Mr. Browning flat. He was now unconscious and unresponsive after the blood to his brain and other organs had abruptly stopped flowing with the loss of a stable heart rhythm. He had died right before our eyes.

While Carrie laid Mr. Browning down, our respiratory therapist, Jorge, who was standing at the head of the bed, reached for a BVM to push air into the patient's lungs since he was no longer spontaneously breathing.

Jorge hooked it up to the oxygen valve on the wall and was about to put it over Mr. Browning's mouth and nose just as I was placing the defibrillator paddles onto his chest. The paddles are like plastic handholds attached to flat metal plates (covered with insulating plastic on the user's side) that are pressed against the patient's chest wall. It has to be firmly applied or else the electrical shock can arc from the paddles to the person's bare skin, potentially burning it.

"Jorge, not now," I said as I nodded him away from what he was instinctively about to do. I knew that the quicker we reestablished Mr. Browning's normal heart rhythm, the better chance he would live through this. Immediate electricity was the highest priority.

"Everyone clear!" I shouted as I looked around the stretcher to be sure no one was in contact with Mr. Browning. I pushed the button on the paddles, and they delivered the electricity into Mr. Browning's chest wall. Muscles in his body twitched from the electrical discharge, but it wasn't as dramatic as what is often portrayed in medical shows.

Keeping the paddles in my hands and standing next to Mr. Browning, I looked up at the heart monitor, simultaneously asking the nurse behind me to charge the paddles again, increasing the charge, in case we needed to deliver another shock.

The rhythm on the monitor remained ventricular fibrillation. The electrical discharge had not changed Mr. Browning's heart rhythm. There was still no blood flow and he remained unconscious. I asked Jorge to check for a pulse at his carotid artery, a large blood vessel in the neck where one can readily feel a pulse if the heart is beating and creating significant forward blood flow.

"No pulse," Jorge said as he looked at me. With the paddles charged, I asked everyone to stand clear again, visually checking to confirm no contact with the patient. I firmly placed the paddles on Mr. Browning's chest wall and shocked him, this time with the more powerful electrical discharge.

Once again, the electricity passed through his chest and upper body, exciting the various muscle fibers, resulting in their contraction and causing another jerking movement of his body.

As soon as this second shock was delivered, I looked up at the cardiac monitor again, hoping to see a stable rhythm replace the chaotic activity that existed just prior to the electrical shock.

Unfortunately, no change.

"Charge it to three sixty," I requested of the nurse. This would increase the electrical charge to its maximum amount. "Pulse?" I asked of Jorge, who had already put his hand on Mr. Browning's carotid artery after the previous shock.

"No pulse," he said. I now delivered the third electrical shock to Mr. Browning's chest and heart. Only a couple of minutes had passed since Mr. Browning had first lost consciousness from the change in his heart rhythm. Anticipating that possibility with his heart attack allowed us to quickly and efficiently respond to the situation.

I looked at the heart monitor after the shock. This time, there was a change. His heart rhythm had returned to its normal appearance with a slightly increased rate. Jorge responded without me asking, "Strong pulse!" He grinned as he said it.

"Give him one hundred milligrams of lidocaine, slow IV push," I said to Julie, one of the nurses next to the medicine cabinet on the other side of Mr. Browning. I continued watching the monitor, hoping we could get the drug into him before his heart rhythm changed again. In this state of "irritability," where the heart is not getting adequate oxygen, a variety of different heart rhythms can appear, some much more serious than others. We had already experienced one of the most dangerous.

Within seconds of Mr. Browning's normal heart rhythm reappearing, he awakened, a little confused and slightly combative as he lay flat on the stretcher.

As I looked at him, assessing whether his mind had cleared enough for me to explain what had happened, I saw a look of sudden panic develop on his face. His eyes opened wide, and he began to shout loudly, "I swallowed it! I swallowed it!" He strove to hurriedly sit upright on the stretcher.

The wild look in his eyes persisted, although the momentary confusion and combativeness seemed to dissipate. He appeared to be processing information correctly now. I was briefly puzzled as to why he was still staring at me with an urgent look of repentance, as though I were a priest hearing his confession.

He passionately repeated himself again and again, "Doc, I swallowed it! I swallowed it!"

Then it dawned on me as I thought about the recent events from his perspective. The last thing he heard was, "Be sure to bite down on the capsule and *not* swallow it!" For him, the minute or two everyone else in the room had experienced was only a second or two for him—his brain had not been logging time while he was unconscious.

Now he had opened his eyes to a completely different situation from what his mind last recorded. He had been sitting when he heard those words, and suddenly—a second or two later—he was lying on the stretcher, people in the room had changed their positions, and he had this new burning sensation across the front of his chest.

And he had swallowed the capsule I told him not to!

His brain was drawing the only logical conclusion it could—all of these sudden changes must have happened because he didn't do what he was supposed to do!

Recognizing the belief his brain had locked on to, I tried to reassure him everything was fine—he didn't need to worry about swallowing the pill. It was not the cause for his confusion or the burning sensation he had experienced.

His mind, however, had firmly connected those two events, and it would be a challenge to alter his perspective. Despite repeated efforts, I don't think I was successful in doing so before he left the emergency department for the cardiac unit upstairs where the cardiologist would now care for him. Thankfully, the new medicine had substantially reduced his chest pain down to a one on the scale.

As they rolled him out of Room 4 in the ER, where he had been resuscitated minutes earlier, he asked the tech to stop for a moment. I was glad to see him reach into his front pants pocket, bring out a package of cigarettes, and shoot a three-pointer across the room, hitting an open trash can.

The visit to the ER turned out to be both a life-threatening and life-changing event for Mr. Browning. It had also been a beneficial experience for Jorge, Julie, and Carrie. None of them had ever witnessed a quick, successful resuscitation like Mr. Browning's. After he left the emergency department, I told the three about a similar scenario I had encountered in the past.

In that ER visit, the patient was relating something to me when his heart suddenly stopped in the middle of his sentence. The resuscitation was similar to Mr. Browning's except that it took only one shock to reestablish the patient's normal heart rhythm. The patient quickly regained consciousness, opening his eyes and literally finishing his sentence from where he had left off immediately before his cardiac arrest. That firmly demonstrated to me the importance of rapid defibrillation, and how the brain, figuratively speaking, didn't skip a beat.

Mr. Browning did well in the hospital and would subsequently go home without any serious complications. I smiled to myself as I thought about how the conversation would go with his cardiologist at the time of his discharge from the hospital. I imagined the doctor explaining to Mr. Browning the importance of taking the blood pressure and cholesterol-lowering medicines in the manner prescribed.

I could hear Mr. Browning's response, "Doc, I've learned the importance of taking medications *exactly* as instructed. Believe me, I know what can happen if I don't!"

Dink Day

A very odd phenomenon periodically occurs in emergency medicine. An unusual grouping of certain illnesses or injuries can inexplicably appear during a given shift in the ER. Perhaps the most recognized pattern involves patients suffering from kidney stones. A number of shifts may go by without any kidney stone cases at all. Then a patient will come in with classic signs of a kidney stone—intense, one-sided flank or lower abdominal pain that causes the patient to be writhing in pain, typically with nausea and occasionally vomiting.

If the ER physician sees a patient with a kidney stone, they are almost guaranteed to see another before their shift ends, oftentimes two more. They seem to come in threes.

Significant trauma cases may also fit such a pattern. Sometimes, abdominal pain patients will similarly come in clusters. Anxiety attacks and hyperventilation cases may likewise appear in groups.

It's as if there is some strange mystical force in the universe that suddenly resonates with other powerful entities—gravity, electromagnetic radiation, tectonic plate movements, rotating neutron stars, dark energy, or another amazing force of nature—to produce these unusual groupings of patient conditions.

One of the strangest—and at times most perplexing—situations is when those forces generate the inexplicable "dink day."

~ ~ ~

It was only nine thirty a.m., but it had already become apparent that today was going to be one of the rare "dink days" in the emergency department.

For those unfamiliar with the sophisticated medical terminology "dink days," they are days in which a good number of patients seem to be suffering from little dinks—small, incidental injuries that people get from time to time as they go through life. Most of the dinks are minor injuries that many people might just look at, let out a groan or loud "ouch," put a Band-Aid on it, and return to whatever they were doing.

Of course, there is a great diversity of people with a breadth of different life experiences that shape their individual perspectives about the seriousness—or not—of an injury and the potential for subsequent problems or "complications."

Think about your initial flight in an airplane. If you experienced turbulence for the first time, you might have gripped the armrest so tightly that your knuckles were white and you were certain the end was coming.

On the other hand, if you've flown many trips, you realize that occasional turbulence is not something to be afraid of, although when the plane hits a pocket and suddenly drops several hundred feet, leaving your heart in your mouth, it's hard not to be afraid. Pilots probably see those incidents as "dinks," while passengers see them quite differently.

Likewise, some cases that emergency physicians might perceive as dinks are understandably reasonable concerns for the patient. For example, the six-month-old baby who accidentally bonks their head. First-time parents may be unsure of whether a little bonk could injure their baby's brain. Without knowing, it is better to be safe than sorry.

On the other hand, the ER physician may occasionally encounter a dink that seems to defy comprehension as to why the patient—or their parents—feel it requires emergency evaluation and treatment.

And sometimes, surprisingly, it's not actually the dink that causes the patient's visit, as I learned on this very unique dink day in the emergency department.

My first patient of the day was David, a cute little five-year-old boy who was brought to the emergency department by his mom, Mrs. Corbin, along with his three-year-old brother Logan.

"No, Mrs. Corbin, I don't think he'll need any stitches. Today must be his lucky day!" I said as I leaned over David, who was sitting on the stretcher in front of me, looking rather solemn—until I made that declaration. He shot a look over at Logan and broke out in a big grin.

I tried to sound sincere and matter-of-fact as I made the remark, attempting to mask my astonishment that Mom had ever considered the possibility of treating the wound with anything other than a drop of antiseptic.

It seems that David and Logan had been playing outside, and David had suddenly turned his head while sitting on the ground and bumped it against an empty wooden box. The resulting injury was a very, very, *very* tiny cut on the right side of his head close to where his hair parted.

Somewhat in disbelief, Mrs. Corbin replied to my statement, "Are you sure it doesn't require stitches or something, Doctor?" She was obviously concerned I was making a poor judgment regarding her son's injury.

I looked closely again at David's blond head. I'm sure Mrs. Corbin must have thought I was seriously reconsidering my decision, which is what I wanted her to believe so she wouldn't feel as if she had asked an unwarranted question.

In reality, I was attempting to mentally measure the total length of this very, very small cut on David's head. At the most, I could only give it a total length of about two millimeters—that's a little less than one-eighth of an inch. But calling it a cut was somewhat of an exaggeration since it didn't even go through the skin. Describing it as a tiny superficial scratch was more accurate.

I continued to maintain my composure when I spoke, "No, Mrs. Corbin, I think he'll do fine without the stitches. It's not a very serious cut." I knew that was a substantial understatement, but again, I didn't want Mom to feel embarrassed about bringing in her son. For future reference, however, I did want to try to enlighten her.

"Are you sure, Dr. Grant? It's so close to his part—I wouldn't want it to become an ugly scar." A look of anguish suddenly appeared on her face.

"Are you sure stitches won't make it look better?" Mrs. Corbin asked, almost pleading now, her hands clasped together in front of her.

I looked at Mrs. Corbin and paused for a moment to make sure I was completely composed in my response to her question.

I could not help but wonder what degree of experience she had with these types of incidents. Perhaps the family was able to employ other individuals to assist with child-rearing and this was the first time in her life she had been required to personally handle this kind of situation.

"Mrs. Corbin, I can assure you that sutures would not improve the final appearance of this wound when it heals. In all probability, this wound will not even leave a trace of a scar since it does not even go through the skin. All that is required is to cleanse it with some antiseptic and it should be fine."

My short dissertation was given in a firm tone of voice, not firm enough to sound annoyed but firm enough to let her know that I was quite sure of my decision and that I had no intention of changing my mind. I looked her straight in the eyes as I spoke every word, hoping she would get the message.

"Oh, Dr. Grant, I am so thankful for that! I was afraid it would surely leave a terrible scar and it is in such a noticeable place. Thank you so much!" She laid her right hand across her chest as if she were catching her breath.

"I'll have the nurse clean it up for us," I said as I turned and left the room. Out front, at the nurses' desk, I asked one of the nurses to care for David and his injury.

Now, of course, a single dink case doesn't make a dink day. There have to be others, such as the young man who came in shortly after Mrs. Corbin with a *literal* paper cut, which was not bleeding and difficult to even see.

Soon thereafter, I had the unique opportunity to make the acquaintance of Mrs. Merritt.

After picking up her chart from the "To Be Seen" box, I walked back to Room 14. As I approached the room, I read the chief complaint typed on the chart by the registration personnel: "Pain in right foot." I looked for the nurses' notes, which usually provide more detailed information, but none were present. I assumed they were still being worked on by the nurse who placed Mrs. Merritt in the room.

I rounded the corner of the hallway and stepped into Room 14, introducing myself to the young woman of about thirty whom I saw before me lying on her back on the stretcher.

"Hello, Mrs. Merritt," I said as I walked to the head of the stretcher and extended my hand toward her. "I'm Dr. Grant." Oddly, she ignored my greeting and simply stared at the ceiling, keeping her arms at her side.

I sat down on the stool next to the stretcher and asked in a low-key, open-ended manner, "What seems to be the trouble with your foot today?" It was the standard, routine question. There are only so many ways to ask it.

I was caught off guard by Mrs. Merritt's response, however, which appeared to be a little testy. "I don't know—that's what I'm here for. You're the doctor, you're supposed to tell me!" With her response she turned her head toward me, offering an exaggerated scowl to register her apparent displeasure.

Although many patients provide those lines in jest, Mrs. Merritt's body language did not suggest she was the jesting type.

I glanced down at her chart, noting the check-in time to see if she might be in a bad mood from waiting too long, a common cause for displeasure in most emergency departments. That didn't seem to be the issue, however. She had only been in the ED for fifteen minutes from the time she signed in at the front desk. That pretty much qualified her for being in the express checkout lane.

I decided to focus on the medical aspect of her visit rather than pursuing the basis for her outlook. Looking back up from the chart and making eye contact with her again, I tried another easy question. "Well, can you tell me when it began hurting, and what you were doing when the pain started?"

With a serious tone of voice and some neutral body language, she responded, "Just this morning, when I dropped a bar of soap on it in the shower."

I waited and listened. Surely, there was more she was about to convey. I was expecting her to possibly tell me she then fell forward as she bent over to pick up the soap, twisting her foot as she fell through the shower door. But no such story followed. She just looked at me.

"Was this a very large bar of soap?" I managed to ask, carefully suppressing the chuckle my mind wanted to add. I was mentally envisioning a bar of soap about the size of a softball.

"No," she said without hesitancy, "It was just the usual size."

I was beginning to feel as though I were missing something, so I sought clarification. "Did you injure your foot in some other way, or was the bar of soap striking your foot the only injury that occurred?"

"No, Doctor," she said, somewhat exasperated, "the bar of soap is what caused my injury." She rolled her eyes as she turned her head so that she was now looking straight up at the ceiling again.

As she lay there, she continued, "I was able to bear the pain initially, although it was severe. However, in the last hour, it became excruciating so I called the ambulance."

That last comment caught me off guard.

I couldn't help myself on that one. "Excuse me?" I said in disbelief. She turned her head toward me again but said nothing—apparently waiting for me to continue.

"I'm afraid I must not be following you," I said. "You dropped a bar of soap on your foot…and you called an ambulance?" I was once again looking her in the eye (and my mouth was probably hanging open a little also).

In somewhat of a derogatory tone, she replied, "Obviously, you have never dropped a bar of soap on your foot." As she spoke, she turned her head so that she was once again looking up at the ceiling. "And I didn't call the ambulance right away. I suffered for two or three hours before I called, and I have a very high threshold for pain."

I always enjoy that line. Most—but certainly not all—who state they have a high threshold for pain usually have a very low threshold for pain. One soon finds out which it is if one must give that person an injection, draw blood for testing, or start an IV. Certainly, each of those procedures hurts to some degree, but if the person is loudly screaming (and cursing) when you stick them, you learn very quickly what their pain threshold truly is.

I paused for a moment before asking Mrs. Merritt any more questions. I was trying to think of any uncommon or unusual medical condition that might explain how she could receive a significant injury from a falling bar of soap.

A disease such as osteogenesis imperfecta, which is associated with brittle bones that easily break, was such a condition. However, she had no past medical history or visible findings to suggest the presence of that disease.

The only other condition I could imagine, which was incredibly unlikely, was that Mrs. Merritt might have a congenital bone cyst in her foot. If the bar of soap happened to strike it at just the right angle, perhaps it could crack the edge of the bone cyst. It was a giant leap, with infinitesimally low odds, but it was all I could imagine.

I got up from my stool and walked down to the foot end of the stretcher, where her injured extremity lay. I had glanced at it when I walked in to see if there was any obvious swelling, deformity, bruising, or abrasion. I had seen none. I now looked more closely to determine if there was even the slightest degree of any of those physical signs. If she did have a fracture in one of the bones on the top of her foot, there should at least be a slight hint of swelling.

There was none.

"Where exactly is your pain, Mrs. Merritt?" I asked before I made any attempt to touch her injured foot.

"On the top of my foot, in the middle," she responded as she lay flat on the stretcher, her left hand now covering her eyes. Most people will usually sit up and show you where it hurts when you ask that question. She chose not to.

I very gently touched the top of her foot near the base of her toes. "Any pain down here?" I asked.

"No," she answered, "but just above that, it is very tender all the way up to my ankle." She kept her hand over her eyes.

I very gently palpated the top part of her foot as I moved up toward the ankle, trying to see if I could feel any swelling that I couldn't recognize visually. Mrs. Merritt responded with an agonizing moan.

I stopped palpating and checked for a pulse and sensation in the foot, both of which appeared to be normal. I then decided to go ahead and send Mrs. Merritt for an X-ray.

In my wildest dreams, I couldn't imagine she might have a fracture, but when the patient is telling you that they are in this much pain, you have to look for reasons that explain the pain, especially when the patient has a "high pain threshold."

Before I ordered the X-ray, however, I asked a few more questions.

"Mrs. Merritt, were you able to walk on your foot after the bar of soap fell on it, or was it too painful?" I moved to a point about half the way up the stretcher now, and Mrs. Merritt took her hand off her face in order to answer me.

"Yes, I walked on it, despite the pain, but it eventually became unbearable." This time, she exhibited no body language as she answered.

"Well, Mrs. Merritt, I really don't think you've broken anything, but since your foot is so tender and you are having so much pain, I'm going to send you for an X-ray to be certain you don't have any underlying bone injury."

I paused for a moment before asking the next question. "Would you like me to give you a shot for the pain before sending you to X-ray?"

The patient's answer sometimes provides additional insight into their degree of discomfort. If people are in severe pain, they will usually accept the offer for an injection. If their pain is not too great, then they will usually decline. Of course, some people will bear all sorts of pain to avoid being stuck with a needle.

"No, as I said, I have a very high threshold for pain, so I will just bear it," she answered in a stoic-sounding voice.

"Very well," I said as I left the room to order the X-ray. I then saw one or two other patients while waiting for her to return from X-ray.

When Mrs. Merritt made it back to Room 14, Judy, one of the ER nurses, brought me Mrs. Merritt's chart and asked if I had seen the X-rays on her yet. I told her I hadn't, but I would do that next.

"Can you believe that story?" Judy asked me as I stood at the nurses' desk writing a prescription for another patient.

"Yeah, that must have been a big bar of soap," I responded as I continued to write.

"Yep, the part about the soap was pretty wimpy, but the part about the shopping was what got me!" Judy said as she turned and was about to walk off.

"Wait a second," I said as I reached out and touched Judy's arm. "What's the part about the shopping? I didn't hear about that."

Judy looked at me and smiled. "You mean she didn't confide in you about that?"

"No, let's have it," I said, not sure what was coming next.

"I guess there are some things that can only be shared between us women," she said as her face lit up with a sparkle in her eyes.

She paused for a moment and then offered the rest of the story. "After she hurt her foot, her husband didn't give her any sympathy, and she got mad at him and left the house to go shopping."

"After about two or three hours of shopping and running up a nice tab, and having lunch at an expensive restaurant with several of her friends, she then called the ambulance to pick her up at the restaurant because it was just too painful for her to drive home!" Judy grinned from ear to ear as she spoke.

I shook my head in disbelief and started to write on a chart, but Judy touched me on my arm to get my full attention. "There's more, Dr. Grant. When I brought her back to Room 14, she insisted I call her husband at work and tell him that she was in extreme pain and that he needed to leave work and come to the emergency room right away. She must have told me that three or four times."

I continued to shake my head in disbelief. "Goodness," was all I could say as I looked at Judy's face brimming with expression.

"Let that be a lesson to you, Dr. Grant. When you get married, you better pay attention to your wife or you'll get a big shopping bill, an expensive dinner bill, an ambulance bill, an ER bill, and you'll have to leave work in the middle of the day!" Judy's eyes twinkled as she delivered her advice.

Judy then turned away to go see another patient, at which time, I heard her additional comment, "And they say men are the stronger sex? I don't think so…" I couldn't help but smile.

I finished writing on my chart and then went to radiology and looked at Mrs. Merritt's X-rays which were, of course, normal. When I went back to Room 14 to give her the good news, she seemed to be in a better mood. Unfortunately, her husband, who was now present, did not convey a very cheerful demeanor. His face was red (I think his blood was boiling), and he didn't say a word to me or his wife the whole time I was in the room.

I told Mrs. Merritt I thought Tylenol would be all she needed for pain. She didn't object or ask for anything stronger. I also informed her she could walk on the injured foot "as pain allowed" since there were no broken bones.

I discharged Mrs. Merritt in the care of her husband, who seemed to have received the greater injury that day.

I then went to see the next patient awaiting me, on what seemed destined to be an incredibly unique and interesting dink day.

Aliens

Like most Friday evenings in the ER, it was busy. It was eleven o'clock, and unfortunately, the typical wave of alcohol-related incidents had already begun.

There were the inebriated patients who had wrecked their cars, along with patients who had been injured by drunk drivers. Then there were patients who had suffered the wrath of intoxicated, agitated individuals who had assaulted their spouses, friends, or children. There were also those who had become too tipsy and made themselves easy targets for people who prey on unsuspecting and incapacitated individuals.

Sadly, there were also the teenagers who had become intoxicated with alcohol for the first time, becoming wild, belligerent, or comatose and were brought in by concerned friends or parents.

In addition, we also had the infrequent chronic alcoholic who was primarily looking for a clean, safe, comfortable place to sleep for a few hours. They often had broad, vague complaints requiring a detailed workup for a host of potential alcohol-related diseases.

This category of illnesses and injuries was why I didn't really care for Friday- and Saturday-night shifts in the ER at a larger hospital. One had to witness the self-inflicted physical, emotional, and social effects of alcohol abuse as well as its impact upon innocent victims, sometimes destroying lives or creating a lifetime of devastating consequences. It was an ongoing tragedy that our society—and, to some degree, the legal system—allowed to exist and, sadly, even flourish.

Of course, there were also plenty of non-alcohol-related illnesses and injuries—the child with a sudden fever, the man with the twisted ankle he feared might be broken, the woman who had deeply cut her hand while preparing a meal, along with a host of other commonly encountered problems.

It would be nice if I had Rollerblades, I thought as I rounded the corner of the hallway, moving as quickly as I could to see the next patient. One of the greatest concerns in the emergency room is the patient whom you have not yet seen. Nurses triage patients entering the ER, trying to discern who is most ill or potentially ill to ensure they are seen before others who are less seriously ill or injured.

Sometimes, however, a patient comes in with complaints that don't trigger the cognitive alarm system alerting one to the time bomb of disease ticking inside the patient's body. "Just a little indigestion" is one of the classics.

I rapidly scanned the chief complaints of the three charts in the "To Be Seen" rack, having just finished the exam of a grossly intoxicated teenager who had run through a plate glass door, not realizing its existence in his state of inebriation.

I mentally crossed my fingers, hoping we would have no more alcohol-related complaints in this group of three. I thought I might be starting to smell like alcohol at this point, especially after caring for patients who couldn't keep their stomach contents in their stomachs.

When I saw the complaint on the first chart, I reassessed my preferences for patient complaints. It simply said "worms." I hurriedly looked at the two that followed—"ankle injury" and "leg laceration." It appeared that "worms" would be my next encounter. I glanced at the patient's age—five years old.

Out of the many illnesses and injuries emergency medicine docs confront, "worms" was not on my favorites list. If I saw only one case every twenty-five years, it would be OK. That perspective was due in part to my past experiences with the creatures. Even though I tried to prevent it, my mind promptly replayed the last one.

It had been a middle-aged woman who came in with a complaint of an "alien" living inside her. When I talked with her, she was frantic, almost psychotic. I did my best to be reassuring and tried to calm her down, to which she eventually responded. I explained that having worms was actually not that uncommon and we had medicine that would take care of the issue. However, when she reached into the large bag she had brought in to show me a gallon-size jar containing the largest and longest tapeworm I had ever seen, I wanted to freak out myself!

I could certainly understand why she had panicked at the sight of that creature in the toilet. It was easy to imagine how one might think they were possessed by an alien creature!

I pushed that mental replay out of my mind and headed toward Room 2 for my next "worm encounter." I pulled back the drape to find a very distraught mom standing next to the stretcher, her child curled up on it in a fetal position. I could tell from Mom's face that she felt the same way about worms as I did, and they had infested her innocent child!

"Oh my gosh! I'm so glad you're here, Doctor," she said before I had a chance to introduce myself. "My son has worms!" It seemed as though the woman was confessing to a terrible crime that had weighed on her mind and soul for so long she could not wait to come clean with the truth. After she blurted out the words, she appeared to experience some immediate relief, having shared her dark secret with someone who might be able to remedy the situation.

"I have no idea how he got them!" It was as if Mom were feeling a degree of guilt over her son being infected with worms. It's similar to when parents discover their child has head lice. Yet, with worms, that anxiety, guilt, concern, etc. is magnified by a factor of about one hundred! I suppose it's because they are *inside* your child rather than just on the outside. And they look a lot grosser.

Of course, anyone can get worms, regardless of their physical, financial, or social status. Depending on the type of worm, they can enter the body in a variety of different ways. For tapeworms, like my previous lady with the jar, it typically comes from eating inadequately cooked meat, which is why all my burgers and steaks are *well done*!

Of course, as a parent, one can't help but feel as though one has failed in some way, leading to this situation.

"Well, Mrs. Caruthers, I think we can cure this little guy of his traveling partners once we know which kind we are dealing with," I said, trying to reassure and calm our frazzled mom as well as our five-year-old patient, Joey.

Unfortunately, my mind was working against me. It was trying to display from memory all the pictures of the many types of ugly, alien-like worms I had studied in medical school, with their sinister-looking mouths; long, segmented bodies; or whiplike appearance. They were all gross looking.

I pushed those images aside, attempting to maintain my focus, although it did require some mental discipline. Like Mrs. Caruthers, I was not fond of worms. Of course, I didn't allow any hint of that perspective to be witnessed by Mom or Joey.

"Have you seen what they look like?" I asked, knowing quite well she had or she wouldn't be so hysterical.

"Yes, they are small white *wormy* things that are about this long," she said as she held up her hand with about half an inch of distance between her index finger and thumb. You could tell she was starting to feel much better, knowing she had an ally in her fight against the alien creatures attacking her child.

"That sounds like pinworms," I said as the name *Enterobius vermicularis* returned to my consciousness from somewhere deep in the recesses of my memory. That was the scientific name I would need to look up to identify the proper drug dose to treat her child. Thankfully, it had been a while since I'd last written a prescription for this ailment.

Of course, it was important to confirm Mom's description of the worms so we could be sure to prescribe the right medication. Pinworms frequently appear in the evening as they crawl out from the patient's anus, at which time they can be seen.

Oftentimes, parents discover the worms near bedtime when the child complains of his bottom itching. I can only imagine Mom's initial response when she looked at Joey's bottom. Not only must it have freaked her out, I imagine her reaction also freaked out Joey.

"OK, Joey, let's take a look at these little fellas," I said, avoiding the term "worms." Joey's appearance was that of the typical five-year-old kiddo—skinny with bony extremities. He also had soft eyes and sandy-colored hair. You could tell that somehow he also felt guilty about the worms, even though he had no understanding of what was going on.

"How about giving me a look at your other end, partner?" I asked as I tousled his blond hair.

Obediently, and without any coaching from Mom, the little five-year-old rolled over onto his stomach, pulled his knees up underneath him and raised his little bottom up in the air. His body looked like an island mountain rising up from the ocean of white paper that covered the stretcher beneath him.

"Let's take down the Scooby-Doos so we can get a look at these fellas," I said as I pulled down his underwear with the famous cartoon character printed all over them. I was amazed at how cooperative and unafraid the little boy was. I think he perceived from his mom's reaction that something terrible had happened and she was very upset about it. Not knowing if he had done something wrong may have removed any potential resistance to requests. He never offered any complaints or did anything other than cooperate fully.

After I got his undies down, I put a hand on each cheek of his buttocks and gently spread them apart. There before me was a whole collection of white-colored worms that tapered to a point on each end, all about one-half inch long.

Some were standing on end, wiggling in the air as if they were waving at me. Others were crawling out from the opening of his anus as if they had some destination they were hurrying to.

A brief wave of nausea suddenly engulfed me as I felt perspiration break out across my brow. *Ugh, I hate worms!*

I let go of Joey's cheeks and tried to collect myself. "Yes, ma'am. Pinworms, all right." I internally struggled to maintain my composure. For a brief moment, I wanted to run out of the room and heave up. Once again, I tried to be reassuring to Joey's mom. "We'll be able to take care of these little critters. I'll first need to calculate a dose for the medicine, and then I'll write you a prescription for it since we don't carry it here in the emergency room."

In an effort to alleviate any guilt Mom might be feeling I explained how her son had contracted the parasites, noting it was a common occurrence in young school-aged children. Typically, microscopic pinworm eggs are unwittingly ingested through contact with an infected child or through contaminated clothing or surfaces. I then provided general hygiene precautions for the rest of the family, including hand washing before meals and laundering of clothing and bed linens in hot water.

I also told her where she could find an all-night pharmacy, knowing there would be no way she would take her child home again until she had some powerful potion to counteract the alien worms trying to take up residence in her child (even though he had probably had them for several days). But I would have had the same reaction!

With great relief, she thanked me. I could tell she wanted to give me a big hug, but she restrained herself. Clearly, she was very appreciative that this awful revelation had been addressed and would soon be over.

After receiving her prescription, she headed for the exit to the ER, the angst of the evening's discovery now alleviated.

Unfortunately, I wasn't so lucky. I returned to the all-night battle with the evil forces of excess alcohol—caring for the casualties of those imbibing it as well as those who had the misfortune to come in contact with the partakers.

But at least the worms were now behind me…

Unbelievable

I thought the lady on the phone hadn't understood me, so I briefly repeated the medical status of my patient. Her response was that she clearly understood the situation, but it didn't change anything. At first, I was incredulous—my mouth must have been gaping open. That feeling swiftly transitioned into frustration and then began growing into anger.

Mia was a young girl who had been brought to the ER by her neighbor. Her reason for coming was apparent as soon as one saw her, which I did from across the emergency room. Sally, one of the ER nurses had gone outside at the ambulance entrance to help Mia from the car into a wheelchair, and then into the ED. Sally was taking her to Room 15, which was closest to the ambulance entrance and the nursing station.

I quickly crossed the ER to Room 15. As I opened the door, Sally had just helped Mia from the wheelchair onto the gurney, where she was now in a reclining position after Sally had raised the head end of the stretcher to about forty-five degrees. Mia leaned back against the elevated part of the stretcher, her legs lying on the flat portion.

The eight-year-old girl was gently supporting her left arm by holding her right hand under her left elbow. Her left forearm was grossly deformed. Rather than appearing straight from the elbow to the hand, at its midportion it took an ugly thirty degree turn upward. It was sickening to look at it.

Clearly, Mia must have landed with a substantial degree of force at just the wrong angle for it to snap her forearm and force it into its current crooked position. As I entered the room, Sally spoke.

"Dr. Grant, this is Mia. She fell off her bicycle and landed on her outstretched arm." Sally spoke in a controlled, even tone of voice without emotion as she positioned a pillow on Mia's lap to better support the broken arm.

Sally was an exceptional, experienced nurse. I loved working with her. She knew that her emotive response to the injury could make Mia more anxious and distressed, or more calm. She then slipped an ice pack between the pillow and Mia's arm to help decrease the swelling that was developing.

I stepped forward to Mia's stretcher wanting to reassure her that as terrible as it looked, it would soon be OK.

"Mia, I'm very sorry about your fall. I know your arm hurts a lot right now, but we're going to give you some medicine to take away a lot of that pain and make you more comfortable." Sally was nodding her head in affirmation as we both stood next to Mia, doing our best to comfort her.

"We're going to take really good care of you." I knelt down on the floor so I could look slightly upward into her eyes as she sat on the stretcher with her head bowed. "We'll be able to fix your arm so that it will look just like it did before the bike accident and will work just as well as ever."

I softly asked Sally if Mia's parents were at the ER yet, and she quietly shook her head no. The neighbor had brought Mia to our hospital since it was so close to her house.

"Mia, do you know if you have any allergies to any medicines or if you have ever had a problem with any medicines before?" I didn't anticipate Mia would know, but it was worthwhile to ask.

Although Mia had rivers of tears streaming down her face, she was quietly sobbing rather than wailing, and did her best to answer my question. That caused me to empathize all the more with her terrible situation.

"No, sir," she said between her sobs.

"Sally, can you check with the neighbor in the waiting room to see if she knows of any drug allergies or medical conditions Mia might have?" Sally nodded and then turned to leave the room. Before she made it out, I had a second request.

"Also, if you don't get any contraindications, please draw up thirty milligrams of Demerol and twelve and a half milligrams of Phenergan to give IM." With that last request, Sally stopped just as she was about to exit the room, turning back toward me with a question in her eyes. I knew what it was, and before she asked, I offered the answer.

"In this setting, I believe we have implied consent," I said. Sally smiled, content I had read her mind and provided the additional information. She then disappeared behind the door.

Sally knew that some might assert we didn't have "consent to treat" Mia since she was a minor and we had not yet been able to contact an adult relative. There was a legal concept known as "implied consent," which I felt fit this situation. Implied consent, as I understood it, basically meant that a "reasonable person"—in this case, Mia's adult relatives—would provide consent to treat Mia under these circumstances if they were actually present.

Of course, being a legal issue, it could be argued that it was not appropriate in this setting since Mia's life was not in danger. Some doctors might choose to wait to administer the medicine, concerned that they may be placing themselves in legal jeopardy if they didn't have the parents' consent to treat their child. If there was any type of adverse reaction to the medicine, the doctor, nurse, and hospital could all be sued by the parents for administering it without their consent.

While there was a small risk for an allergic reaction, we were prepared to readily treat it if necessary. Waiting an unknown amount of time to obtain the information while Mia was suffering in such pain was not a reasonable option in my mind. If it was my daughter in this setting, I would want the doctor to treat her with pain medicine.

That was the type of reasonable guideline many ER docs use when making the decision to treat. It's a scenario that doctors in emergency medicine frequently encounter. We always try to focus on the patient's condition and needs rather than worry about the twenty-twenty hindsight that will be offered by the lawyers if the outcome is not as desired. Sadly, it is a risk emergency medicine physicians carry too often despite their best efforts in treating the patient.

With Sally gone to retrieve the pain medicine and ask about allergies, I stood up next to the stretcher as I asked Mia several more questions about her fall and whether she was hurting anywhere else.

As I did so, I gently examined her forearm looking closely at the skin overlying the middle part of her forearm to determine whether it had been punctured by the broken bones. Thankfully, there was no evidence the skin had been torn or penetrated, thereby decreasing the potential for subsequent infection.

I also gently checked her pulse, skin color, and sensation downstream (toward the hand) to be sure the blood vessels were providing adequate blood flow and the nerves were working properly.

Mike, one of the EMTs who worked in the ER as a tech, had come into the room to help. I asked him to go to the orthopedic room to get some splinting materials we could use to help stabilize Mia's badly broken and deformed arm once the pain medicine had a chance to take effect.

Just as Sally came back into the room with the medicine, Mia's father, Mr. Harrison, arrived also. While he tried very hard to keep his face from reflecting the anguish he felt when he saw his daughter, it was clear he wanted to burst out crying. He knelt down next to the stretcher with his face close to Mia's and gently began to stroke her long auburn hair, telling her it would all be OK.

After hearing from Dad that Mia didn't have any allergies or medical problems, I explained that we would like to give Mia a shot of pain medicine to make her more comfortable. Once the medicine had a chance to work, we would take her to X-ray to get some pictures to see how the broken bones looked on the inside.

Mr. Harrison nodded his head in affirmation.

It wasn't very long after the injection that Mia began to experience some significant pain relief. Mike and I then gently applied splinting material to her forearm, providing better stability so the broken bones would not easily move. With the grossly angulated fracture, it wasn't an easy task, but we were able to complete it without much discomfort to Mia.

The radiology technician came to the room to take Mia to X-ray. As he rolled her to the adjacent department to get the images, I spoke to Mr. Harrison as we walked together to the nurses' station.

"I'll take a look at Mia's X-rays as soon as they're done, but please know that she will likely need surgery to adequately fix the breaks. We won't be giving her any fluids or medicine by mouth because of the potential need for surgery."

Mr. Harrison nodded and thanked me for looking after Mia. He then said he needed to make some phone calls, so I excused myself to see another patient or two while we waited for Mia and the X-ray films to come back.

After seeing an asthma patient and getting him started on a breathing treatment, I swung by X-ray to see if Mia's films were done and up for viewing. They were, and it was indeed a nasty break that would require surgery to adequately get the bones—and their fragments—back into position. I walked back to the ER from the X-ray department and saw Mr. Harrison at the nurses' station talking to someone on the phone. When he saw me, he asked the person with whom he was conversing to hold for a minute.

As I approached the nursing desk, Mr. Harrison informed me he was talking to his insurance company and they'd told him we couldn't operate on Mia at our hospital. Somewhat perplexed, I told him that the orthopedic surgeon group that was on call to the emergency room was an excellent group and they had a surgeon who specialized in operating on fractures of the arm and hand.

Mr. Harrison related that information to the insurance company as I stood at the nurses' station, writing some orders on a couple of other patients I had seen while Mia was in X-ray.

"Would you hold again, please, so I can talk to the doctor?" Mr. Harrison said into the phone. Angela, the unit secretary, put the call on hold.

"Doc, it's not a question of whether the hospital and doctors have the capability, they are telling me they will only pay for her care if Mia is operated on at a different hospital—one of 'their' hospitals." His eyes had become very misty.

I had encountered that situation a few times previously, and usually, once the insurance company understood that it was emergency surgery—not a scheduled elective operation—then they would OK the surgery. I related that to Mr. Harrison, who then talked to the insurance person again, explaining the situation in detail. He didn't seem happy with the conversation taking place. He asked them to hold again and then asked me if I would talk with them.

"Certainly," I said, thinking we could clear it up quickly.

Taking the phone from Mr. Harrison, I said, "Hello, this is Dr. Grant. I'm the emergency medicine physician caring for Mia Harrison. To whom do I have the pleasure of speaking?" I didn't really think this was going to be enjoyable, but I hoped that introduction might get us off to a good start.

"This is Samantha Everly of the Quality and Compassion Insurance Company." The statement was followed by silence, so I continued.

"Ms. Everly, Mia has a thirty-degree angulated and comminuted fracture of both the radius and ulna at the mid-forearm that will require surgical reduction. Her neurovascular exam is intact currently, but with this degree of deformity and ongoing swelling, it could become compromised, which is why we would like to get her to surgery as soon as possible."

I paused briefly before continuing. "Is there any additional information you need, or may we contact the orthopedic surgeon and OR team to get her to surgery?"

"I am not in need of any additional information, Doctor. Mr. Harrison can choose to have his daughter cared for at your hospital if he wishes. As I've explained to him, it is his choice. However, if he chooses to have the operation there, he will be totally responsible for the bill. We will not pay for any services provided."

Her response surprised me. Actually, it floored me. Delaying the necessary treatment of a patient who needs emergency surgery is clearly not in the best interest of the patient. Surely, I thought, Ms. Everly had not fully grasped the situation.

"I'm sorry, perhaps I didn't adequately describe Mia's condition. The swelling associated with this degree of injury could potentially compromise the blood flow to her hand as well as the function of the nerves that make her hand work. The sooner she is operated on to reduce and stabilize the fracture, the sooner that risk can be addressed." I hoped that if Ms. Everly understood the risk associated with delayed treatment, she would grasp the necessity of urgently getting her to surgery.

"I understand, Doctor. That does not change our policy."

I couldn't believe it! It was clear to me I would not make any progress with Ms. Everly. I needed to talk with someone else, ideally someone with a degree of medical knowledge.

"Ms. Everly, may I speak with a supervisor or a clinician to discuss this further? I'm afraid there's not a clear understanding of Mia Harrison's condition." While frustrated, I was careful to not let it be evident in my voice.

"No, there is no supervisor or clinician," was her curt response, which she followed with her reiteration of Mr. Harrison's choice to do as he wished but that any treatment Mia received at our hospital would be out of his pocket. The insurance company would not pay for any of it.

I was astonished. Insurance companies negotiated prices with hospitals and physician groups as part of their "network," and if one didn't agree to their proposed payment, the doctors and/or hospital were classified as "out of network" by the company. That usually meant a different level of deductible or copay for the insured, but I had never heard of an insurance company simply refusing to pay for emergent surgery on patients brought to a hospital's emergency room.

Recognizing that Mr. Harrison may have no option but to transfer his daughter to another hospital, I asked what hospitals were potential destinations for a transfer. Ms. Everly informed me there was only one and provided its name. I immediately recognized that it was downtown and would require about a thirty-minute drive in the best of traffic. But it was now five in the afternoon, which would probably double the transport time.

"Do you not have a closer facility to which she can be transferred?" I asked, attempting to clearly voice my concern. "At this time of the day, such a transfer will delay her care by at least a couple of hours."

In addition to the actual drive time, transfers require substantial communication between all parties, with copies of X-rays and the medical chart along with government-required paperwork that the patient takes with them. In addition, the clinicians at the receiving hospital would perform a reassessment of the patient once she arrives.

"No." Again a short, curt answer by what appeared to be a completely unsympathetic person who was denying me the opportunity to talk with any other person in her organization.

Recognizing Mr. Harrison and I were out of options, in frustrating defeat, I asked the next question. "Is there a specific ambulance service we need to contact for the transfer?"

If they only allowed one hospital to care for Mia, then I imagined they had a contract with a specific ambulance service. I just hoped it wouldn't take too long for that agency to respond to our location.

Without hesitation, Ms. Everly responded, "In this situation, there is no need for an ambulance. She can be transported by private vehicle," which meant Mr. Harrison's car.

I almost exploded! I couldn't believe this. Ms. Everly was making a medical judgment regarding the transport of a patient, just as she had when she said the surgery could be delayed by at least a couple of hours secondary to the transfer.

I took a moment to compose myself, hoping that the information I was about to provide might change her mind regarding this facet of Mia's care, which was significantly less costly than her surgery. This was basic medical transportation. Knowing an insurance company is all about risk, I tried again to speak their language.

"Just for the record, it is important that I convey to you the following information. Mia Harrison, the patient requiring transport, may become nauseated from the pain of her injury, especially in a moving vehicle. That could cause her to vomit, which could then cause her to get light-headed and pass out, substantially worsening her condition." I paused for a just moment, but not long enough for a response as I further clarified the realistic risk of such a transfer.

"In addition, should such an event take place, it could easily be a distraction to her father, who is the only person now with her. He would be driving her in his 'private vehicle' during rush-hour traffic. Unfortunately, that could result in a vehicular accident, which could injure the occupants and seriously jeopardize Mia's arm if it was further traumatized."

I hoped my identification of these additional risks to "our" patient would cause her to rethink her decisions.

"Dr. Grant," Ms. Everly said, "if you want to drive down with Mr. Harrison yourself, that would be fine, although we will not reimburse you for your assistance. Mr. Harrison can choose to do what he wishes, but, once again, the only treatment we will pay for is what is done once he and his daughter arrive at the hospital we've specified."

I had never encountered this degree of complete disregard for the care of a patient by an insurance company representative. I was stunned. I was also disgusted, frustrated, and brokenhearted for Mr. Harrison and Mia.

"I am disappointed to hear the company's position regarding this patient. Please stay on the line while I talk to Mr. Harrison," I requested. Angela, our secretary at the nurses' station, gladly put the woman on hold again.

I related our exchange, much of which Mr. Harrison heard as he stood next to me while I spoke to the insurance representative. He asked me if I could give him a ballpark idea of the cost of the surgery, clearly struggling, as he was now being forced to make a choice between the family's finances and the pain and risk to his daughter. I told him it was just a gross estimate, but I knew it would be a complicated surgery and it would likely cost at least fifteen to twenty thousand dollars when all the costs were added up. I told him we could try to get a better estimate if it would help.

I hated for him to be in this position. My emotions churned from empathy and sadness to frustration and anger. I felt so terribly bad for him—no one should have to make such a choice.

Mr. Harrison got on the phone again to speak with Ms. Everly. While he did so, I went into Mia's room with one of the nurses to reassess her condition, checking her pulse, skin color, and nerve function in the affected arm. It was all adequate, and her pain medication was still working well.

In anticipation that Mr. Harrison would be forced to take Mia to the other hospital, I asked one of the nurses to see if she could find a hospital volunteer who could go with Mr. Harrison and try to comfort Mia as best she could. Such an action was not in the scope of what our volunteers typically did, but I couldn't think of a better option. And I asked if we could get some pillows to send with the Harrisons to make Mia as comfortable as possible.

I then headed off to see another waiting patient, telling the nurse to let me know once a decision was made so we could do our best to expedite Mia's care.

When I came back to the nurses' station after seeing a patient, Mr. Harrison was there. He reached out his hand to me.

"Thank you, Dr. Grant, for taking care of Mia and trying to help me with the insurance. I'm afraid I need to take her to the other hospital." His eyes were filled with tears, which caused them to well up in my eyes also.

"You're very welcome," I said, my voice cracking. "I'm very sorry we were not able to do more for you both."

I then added something. "If you have any issues related to this transfer, or if there is anything I can help you with regarding the insurance company, please do not hesitate to call me here at the emergency room. I will be happy to help you in any way I can." I could see on his face that he understood what I meant.

He thanked me again and then turned and headed down the hallway to the ambulance exit, where the nurses had already helped Mia into the back seat of their car, which was not very large.

When I asked Angela, the ER secretary, if they had been able to find a volunteer to go with Mia, she told me that

Glenda, one of our ER nurses, who had just finished her shift, happily offered to go.

I smiled when I heard that. Glenda, and pretty much all of our ER nurses, have amazing hearts of gold. I should have known they would step in to fill the void—the very large void this insurance company had no interest in filling.

Our nurses had real compassion for their patients, something the Quality and Compassion Insurance Company clearly did not exhibit for Mia, despite their name. I knew Glenda would be an incredible comfort to Mia and Mr. Harrison, who were taking a trip they should have never been forced to make.

~ ~ ~

I saw Mia more than twenty years ago. Unfortunately, to the dismay of clinicians, the power and impact of insurance companies on the provision of medical care have grown substantially. Decisions about where patients can go for treatment and to what degree they are covered for different types of treatment have become increasingly complex. Trying to understand which doctors and other health care professionals are "in network" versus "out of network" is a continually changing game. Sometimes, particular insurance companies may not even be able to tell the patient with certainty whether a specific provider is in their network on a given day.

This, of course, leaves the patient to figure it out on their own. And, worst of all, when the patient has an emergency, there isn't an opportunity to do the research. A doctor and hospital may have been "in network" yesterday, but today were designated as "out of network" by an insurance company, unbeknownst to the patient.

Perhaps most disturbing for emergency care is a recent approach some insurance companies have begun to utilize. It is a *retrospective* review of the patient's visit to the ER. If a serious diagnosis is ultimately made in the ER, the company *may* provide coverage for the visit. If, on the other hand, the final diagnosis in the ER thankfully turns out to be less dire, the insurance company may choose to *deny* coverage for the ER visit, suggesting that the patient didn't need to go to the emergency room in the first place and should have sought health care in a different setting.

Of course, in this twenty-twenty hindsight determination, the insurance company will decide what qualifies as "serious."

So, if a patient injures their ankle and has significant pain, they may go to the ER to get an evaluation that includes an X-ray. If the patient does have a broken bone, and perhaps requires surgery, then the insurance company's *retrospective* review may consider it serious enough to cover certain costs associated with the visit.

On the other hand, if there is no fracture on the X-ray and the injury is just a significant sprain, then following the insurance company's *retrospective* review, they may choose to deny aspects of coverage for the visit, which leaves the patient to cover most, or all of, the bill out of pocket.

Obviously, the doctor needed to get the X-ray in order to determine whether there was a fracture. This new policy suggests the doctor and the patient should have known what the X-ray would show before it was ordered—clearly, an absurd perspective.

Much worse, however, are complaints such as chest pain. There are many causes of chest pain, a number of which can present with similar symptoms. Some of those causes are truly life-threatening. Others may cause substantial pain or discomfort but are not likely to be lethal. Again, the patient and the doctor won't know for certain until tests are run to determine the underlying cause of the symptoms.

Unfortunately, if the patient's diagnosis is not life-threatening—such as chest pain caused by heartburn (esophageal reflux)—a patient's insurance company, doing a *retrospective* review, may choose to deny coverage for some or all of the cost of the ER visit, suggesting the patient and the doctor should have known the results of the tests before they were ordered.

Such an approach is preposterous. Unfortunately, it will likely discourage some patients from going to the emergency room for serious symptoms they experience, like chest pain or abdominal pain. Not knowing what the ultimate diagnosis may be, the patient may want to avoid the risk of bearing the full cost of an ER visit. Of course, that's supposed to be what people purchase insurance for in the first place.

No doubt this new approach will increase the profits of the insurance companies that use it while creating confusion and frustration for the "insured" who paid their premiums to have "coverage."

Thankfully, not all insurance companies have adopted this arbitrary twenty-twenty hindsight approach. Certainly, there are a select number of reputable companies that provide more clarity and certainty regarding their coverage so that policyholders can understand the coverage they have paid for, allowing them to more confidently access the appropriate health care they need for themselves and their families.

In today's social media climate, perhaps insurance policies and processes like the ones Mr. Harrison and Mia experienced will generate a firestorm of angst against unreasonable practices by some companies. Perhaps our legislators will hear the voice of their constituents more loudly than that of the insurance lobbyists.

Hopefully, such an outcry can generate the necessary change before too many patients suffer as a result of decisions and actions by corporate officers rather than clinicians who care for their patients.

Situations such as these cannot help but remind one of the *Rainmaker*, a book by John Grisham that became a movie with Matt Damon and Danny DeVito. It was a good illustration of an insurance company that focused on profits to the detriment of patients. Unfortunately, it seems that story reflects a perspective that may still be embraced by certain entities today.

It appears the "business of health care" has significantly impaired the opportunity for some patients to receive the care they need.

The Clue

"Headache in Room 1," Linda said as she dropped the patient's chart into the doctor's "To Be Seen" box at the nurses' desk. Then she was off to continue restocking the patient rooms in the ED. It had been a busy night shift, and the staff hadn't finished replacing supplies before the day shift arrived.

Thankfully, this Friday morning had begun at a leisurely pace. It was now nine o'clock, and I had only seen one patient in the previous two hours. I was enjoying the unusually slow start. I hopped up from my chair at the nursing station, grabbed the chart from the rack, and headed to Room 1 as I glanced at the patient record for info.

The patient was an eighteen-year-old male with a chief complaint of "headache." He had no past medical history of any chronic diseases, migraine headaches, recent fever, or any other symptoms—just a headache.

His vital signs revealed a heart rate slightly higher than expected, but that wasn't unusual. Some patients are anxious when seeing a doctor, unsure of what to expect. At times, anxiety can increase a patient's heart rate, respiratory rate, and blood pressure.

I rounded the corner to Room 1 and saw a young man who appeared to be about six feet tall and 220 pounds, leaning against the side of the stretcher. As he raised his eyes to me, I smiled at him, trying to put him at ease.

"Good morning, Sam Battey," I said as I extended my hand to him. "My name is Tom Grant. I'm the emergency medicine physician."

Sam stood up straight and shook hands with a firm grip as he responded with his own, "Good morning."

I pulled up a stool and sat in front of him as he sat down on the stretcher. He didn't appear to be in any distress and did not look ill.

After some initial small talk, I went through my standard line of questioning related to headaches—asking about recent head trauma, stress, anxiety, allergies, fever, sore throat, runny nose, nasal congestion, body aches, sensitivity to light, weakness, numbness, and a number of other conditions as I searched for a clue that might suggest an etiology, or cause for his headache. But I came up empty, which wasn't that unusual. It's not always possible to readily identify an underlying cause.

Sam's situation, however, seemed a little different to me. He was only eighteen years old and his parents hadn't come with him to the ER. Usually, for a teenager with a complaint of headache, someone has to *make* them go see the doctor unless the headache is unusually severe. Sam's was not.

As with all headache patients, I explored the onset, duration, and progression of the headache as I continued the search for clues. Sam had a hard time providing much detail or specificity when answering my questions. In his words, he had "just sort of noticed it" before going to bed last night and it was still there when he got up this morning.

His answers didn't fit with the typical history of someone with a new-onset migraine headache, a cluster headache, a tension headache, a tumor-related headache, a headache from a ruptured blood vessel, or any other type of headache associated with a specific diagnosis.

When I asked Sam one of the key headache questions, "Is this the worst headache you've ever had?" Sam paused for a moment.

"Well, I've never really had a headache that I can remember. So, yeah, I guess this is the worst I've ever had."

Despite his answer, there was no suggestion in Sam's voice, mannerisms, or body language that he was experiencing any significant pain. He seemed comfortable, conversive, and with a friendly and upbeat disposition.

He said the reason he came in was because it "didn't seem normal" to him so he thought he should get it checked out. He had debated with himself whether to even come in, but his parents were out of town and he hadn't been able to check with them. He had a job with good insurance but didn't have a regular doc, so he decided to come to the ER.

Sam didn't pass the eyeball test for being a sick patient. And he had no truly concerning answers to my questions. He looked completely normal.

Yet there were three little things that bothered me.

First, teenage males don't typically come to the doctor for complaints like Sam's unless they might have a hysterical personality. Sam clearly did not.

Second, Sam's heart rate and blood pressure remained mildly elevated, even after we had talked a bit. I had rechecked them myself, and he seemed to be at ease with so sign of anxiousness. That was a little atypical.

Finally, Sam didn't have any kind of individual or family history of headaches. Neither did he have any pattern of symptoms that might suggest one of the common reasons for a headache.

Usually, a good patient history allows a physician to create a "differential diagnosis," a list of possible diseases or injuries that might explain the patient's symptoms. Working with that list, the physician performs a physical exam and perhaps some tests, looking for findings or test results that can exclude some diagnoses on the list while elevating the likelihood of others. After considering all the available information, the physician then arrives at a probable diagnosis and institutes treatment for the disease or injury.

In Sam's case, there weren't any good candidate diagnoses to put on the list.

"Well, Sam, we need to do a good physical exam to see if we can identify any findings that might help explain your headache," I said as I reached over to the linen cart, grabbed a rolled-up patient gown, and tossed it to him. "Strip down to your undies and put on the gown with the opening in the back. I'll be back shortly." Then I headed out of the room.

After quickly seeing another patient who had come back to the ER for a wound check, I returned to Room 1. Sam was now in his patient gown sitting on the middle of the stretcher near its edge.

I began Sam's exam with a focus on his neurological system, looking for any subtle abnormality that might tip me off to some veiled cause for his headache. But I found none. A comprehensive neurological exam was completely normal, which was reassuring.

I then continued my search for other potential abnormalities as I began to methodically examine Sam's other body systems.

Using a handheld ophthalmoscope, I looked at Sam's retina and optic nerve for any evidence of swelling. If there is an increased degree of pressure in the fluid surrounding the brain, at times, it may be visualized at the back of the eyes. Sam's retina and optic nerve appeared normal in both eyes.

Early infections of the central nervous system can sometimes suggest their presence with slight neck stiffness or discomfort when flexing one's head forward. Sam had none.

I marched through the other body systems but found nothing. Only the examination of his skin remained. I asked him to lie down on the stretcher and began to visually scan his skin, looking for any clue that might suggest a cause for his headache. Everything appeared normal.

He still had his socks on, however. In my typical obsessive approach, I felt the need to check his feet as well. The left side of my brain was reminding me of a couple of skin findings—uncommon yet possible—that might point to a disease process that hadn't yet been discovered.

"Sam, can I slip your socks off and check your feet?" I asked.

"Sure," Sam responded, probably wondering if his doctor had lost his mind. I could imagine his thoughts: *Why would a doctor be looking at my feet when my problem is at the opposite end of my body?*

I slipped off his socks and carefully examined the skin of his feet. The only abnormality I noticed was a small purplish dot on the end of his left big toe. It was only about one-sixteenth of an inch in diameter—like a freckle except it was light purple in color. It was what I had carefully been looking for—a petechia. When I saw it, however, I wondered if that was really what it was. There are other causes for having a single purplish dot on the end of one's toe.

If I could find more than one of the purple dots, I would be more confident they were indeed petechiae (more than one petechia). If petechiae were present, it would suggest a rather ominous diagnosis to consider. I quickly scanned the rest of his skin again, looking at his feet but also his hands and the rest of his body. I found no others, making me doubt the significance of the single purple dot I had found on his toe.

But I couldn't dismiss it. I looked for other potential explanations for the small purple dot. I searched for scrapes or bruises or anything else that might suggest it was just a tiny bruise. After all, it was right on the end of his big toe. He could have easily bumped it against something and never even noticed.

"Sam, have you ever seen this little purple dot on the end of your toe?" I asked, hopeful he might tell me it was a little birthmark he had all his life. But I knew that wasn't likely.

"I can't say that I have," was his response. "Of course, I suppose it could have always been there and I never paid attention to it." With a quizzical look, he asked, "Why, what difference does a dot on my toe make?" Again, I imagined that Sam felt he had an oddball of a doctor checking him over.

Simultaneously, a short video clip flashed through my mind in which I saw several of my colleagues laughing and knee-slapping as they incredulously said to me, "You worked up a kid for what you thought was a single petechia on his big toe?"

In that moment, part of me felt I might be exaggerating the significance of the small purple freckle. But part of my brain also refused to ignore it. When I added it to the other three things about Sam's visit that didn't fit, I felt compelled to work Sam up. While one might be able to explain away each item alone, the combination crossed a pretty low but significant threshold for me to consider a disease that could be responsible for both the purple dot and the headache—bacterial meningitis. It is a disease that can kill, and it can kill *quickly*.

I knew because I had seen it in young children. I had witnessed how rapidly the disease could spread, overwhelming the body's defenses and causing the patient to suddenly deteriorate, sometimes dying within twenty-four hours of arriving at the hospital.

Yet there were no other clues that supported the diagnosis of meningitis. I had looked for them but they weren't present. Since Sam wasn't feeling sick at the moment, I thought it might be a challenge to get him on board with my concerns.

"I'm worried this purple-looking freckle might actually be a very early sign of an infection that is causing your headache." I could tell Sam didn't know what to think. He was just a teenager and had no real context within which to put this information.

I continued. "While it may seem innocuous, it could be the initial indication of a very serious disease process that can cause you to become very ill, very suddenly."

I could now see the concern on Sam's face.

"We need to do some additional testing, and while we wait for the results, I'm going to start you on some antibiotics just to be safe."

I explained to Sam that we would draw blood for testing and would do a CT scan of his head, possibly followed by another test, depending upon the initial results. I didn't want to use the words "lumbar puncture" or "spinal tap" at this point. I was afraid it would scare him more, maybe even cause him to reject the testing process and decide to leave the ER with a plan to wait until he could contact his parents for their input. If my suspicion about meningitis was accurate, such a decision could cost him his life.

"If you're OK with it, while we're running the tests, I would like to try to contact your parents, just to let them know you're here getting some tests run."

I had communicated all of the information to Sam in a matter-of-fact manner, hoping to not frighten him by injecting too much emotion. After all, I wasn't completely sure about the real potential for meningitis myself. In fact, I thought it was improbable the results would actually support that diagnosis. But I could not simply dismiss that unlikely possibility. The risk was too great. Missing a diagnosis of early bacterial meningitis could lead to Sam's death or significant, permanent disability. That would be tragic.

"Any questions before we get started?" I asked, trying to maintain Sam's confidence in this doc he had just met, who wanted to run a bunch of tests because of a dot on his toe along with his headache.

"I don't think so," Sam answered.

I headed out to the nurses' desk, found Linda, and told her my concerns and what we were going to do. I impressed upon her the need to frequently reevaluate Sam and let me know if *anything* changed—especially his cognitive function or if any more skin lesions appeared.

Linda and I worked really well together and had mutual respect for each other's talents. I could tell from her open mouth and the empty look in her eyes, however, that she thought I had gone off the deep end. There was a tiny voice in the back of my mind wondering the same thing.

She knew I was meticulous, but I think she felt I had overthought this one. I could see the unspoken question on her face: *Bacterial meningitis in a healthy-looking teenager who is acting completely normal? For real?*

After her initial shock wore off, Linda jumped right in and did exactly what I had asked, treating it with all the seriousness I had conveyed. She got the IV antibiotics on board rapidly, which was the most important first step, and then started a second IV in case we needed to administer IV fluids for a drop in Sam's blood pressure.

Simultaneously, she had drawn his blood for the lab tests and was in the process of taking him to radiology for a *stat* CT scan. I had called radiology to let them know my concern about meningitis and that we needed the scan ASAP—ahead of anyone else who wasn't critically ill.

The scan would help rule out any "mass effect" or "early brain swelling" that could be a contraindication to performing the next test, which was the spinal tap. Although his optic nerves and retinas did not show any evidence of brain swelling, the CT scan might provide subtle evidence of it.

During the testing, Ericka, our ER secretary, had continued to try to reach Sam's parents but had been unsuccessful. I was now in Room 1 preparing the equipment and supplies for doing the lumbar puncture as soon as Sam returned from the CT scan.

As I got out the lumbar puncture tray and the sterile gloves, for a split second, I thought about how foolish my urgency would seem if everything came back normal. But the logical part of my brain swiftly dismissed it. Normal or not, the testing needed to be done.

Doubt returned as my mind continued the intellectual debate. If only there had been several of the purple dots, I would have had more confidence. But the single one on the end of his toe should be enough to raise the alarm, especially with the other findings—although subtle—that didn't fit.

Just as I finished arranging the items for the lumbar puncture on the Mayo stand (a movable metal table), Linda came wheeling the stretcher through the open door to Room 1 with one of the radiology technicians helping her. I could see on her face something had changed. She had a look of concern.

From the doorway, she said, "He's not thinking as clearly," as she hurriedly moved the stretcher to its place in the room and locked its breaks.

Alarm bells immediately began clanging loudly and rapidly in my brain. There was no question now. This young man had bacterial meningitis, and he would be in for the battle of his life—*literally*. Everything now needed to shift into an even higher gear. We needed to be prepared for a number of potentially life-threatening complications that might show at any moment.

I hit the intercom button on the wall, turning my back to Sam so he wouldn't hear my words. "Ericka, I need the report from radiology *stat*! And please call Dr. Reed. Tell him I need him in the ER right away. Tell him I have a patient with bacterial meningitis and initial antibiotics are on board."

I knew Dr. Reed would be seeing patients in his office at this time of day, but I also knew that if I called him with this information, he would hastily head to the ER, recognizing how critically ill a patient with this disease could be.

After speaking with Ericka via the intercom, I reassessed Sam to determine whether I would be able to do the spinal tap. Patients with meningitis can become very confused and combative.

To check Sam's cognitive status, I asked him a few questions as I put on my sterile gloves to perform the procedure. Clearly, he was not as alert and communicative as he had been earlier. It was not a prominent change, but it was an undeniable difference. His blood pressure and heart rate remained stable, but that could suddenly change also.

I told Linda I was going to start the lumbar puncture preparation, hoping to hear from the radiologist before inserting the spinal needle. If one does the procedure while there is significantly elevated pressure inside the skull, it can potentially have devastating consequences for the patient. I greatly desired the additional confirmation there was no evidence of increased pressure that would preclude the procedure.

If we could perform the spinal tap, it would enhance our ability to identify the specific bacteria causing the meningitis. That would allow us to select the most effective antibiotics for killing the bacteria as rapidly as possible.

Sam's mental status and cooperation could deteriorate swiftly, however. Time was critical. If I didn't get the verbal report from the radiologist by the time Sam was positioned for the procedure with the local anesthetic administered, I decided I would start without the CT results. That window was two minutes or less.

I asked Linda to help me, knowing that Sam might not be able to cooperate to the degree desired. I was concerned he might become agitated from various stimuli, including the local anesthetic that would be injected into the skin of his lower back using a small needle. If he did start to thrash about during the procedure, I would have to hastily remove the needle from its location near the spinal cord to prevent the possibility of neurological damage.

Sam was now lying on his side on the stretcher, his back toward me. The side rail on my side of the stretcher was in the down position. Linda was on the opposite side from me, leaning over the raised bed rail on her side while also leaning over Sam's body.

Linda was encouraging Sam to stay in the fetal position we had placed him in, speaking in a calm and soothing voice. She had tucked her right arm behind and under Sam's neck as she leaned over him, the other arm behind and under his knees.

She would try to help him stay in the flexed, balled-up position as best she could. With his size, however, it would probably be momentary at best.

I had already put antiseptic solution onto Sam's lower back in the location where the spinal needle would enter the skin. I explained to Sam what I was doing as I injected the local anesthetic into the skin where the spinal needle would soon follow.

"Ouch," Sam verbalized as he also flinched from the mild sting of the local anesthetic. But he remained in the fetal position with Linda's assistance.

While the local went to work, I placed a sterile sheet with a hole in its center over Sam's back. I now had the spinal needle in my hand, about to insert it, when the radiologist came through the door to Room 1.

"No evidence of increased ICP," Dr. Hayes said, referring to Sam's intracranial pressure. "However, there is the slightest increase in density of the fluid, supporting the diagnosis of meningitis."

The radiology group at our hospital was a remarkable team of very knowledgeable and extremely competent physicians. At times, they would identify very subtle findings that other radiologists with whom I had worked with in the past did not often pick up.

"Thanks, Tim," I said as I looked up to Linda from the stool I was sitting on to see if she was ready. If Sam's mental status deteriorated further, we both might be in for a wild ride, but Linda would feel the brunt of it first.

She nodded her head in affirmation. In that flash of an instant, her nod reminded me of a bronco rider who'd just finished wrapping the rope around their hand as they sat on the stallion, now signaling for the cowboys to open the gate and let the ride begin.

I hoped there would be no bucking from Sam. We needed the spinal fluid.

I was able to briskly navigate the long needle between the bony processes of the lumbar vertebrae and into the spinal canal. Sam moved a little during the insertion, but Linda was able to help restrain him. I removed the stylet from within the needle so that spinal fluid could now drip through the hollow needle and into the sterile test tubes.

The spinal fluid collection took only a minute or two, but it seemed much longer than that, due in part to the building anxiety that Sam would become uncooperative at any moment. As I finished the fluid collection and was removing the needle from Sam's back, he became more agitated and confused. With the needle out, we rolled Sam onto his back and tried to reassure him.

"Linda, can you recheck his vital signs?" I asked as I picked up the four tubes containing spinal fluid to send them to the lab *stat.* Thankfully, the spinal fluid grossly appeared clear, like tap water, which meant we had caught the infection early. That fact would help Sam's prognosis for the life-threatening disease with which he now suffered.

After stepping out of the room to hand the tubes of spinal fluid to Ericka, I reentered Room 1.

"BP one thirty over seventy, heart rate one twenty, respirations eighteen, O2 sat 98 percent," Linda called out to me. Sam's BP had dropped slightly and his heart rate had bumped up a little. For now, they were within an anticipated range.

As I was taking off my sterile gloves, Dr. Jay Reed came into the room.

"Looks like my timing was perfect," he said with a smile, referring to the fact that we had already done most of the initial evaluation and treatment, including the spinal tap. Sometimes, when the ER is very busy and the timing of the spinal tap is not as crucial as it was with Sam, the neurologist might perform the lumbar puncture. In Sam's case, however, it could not wait.

Having just cleared the last hurdle in Sam's initial evaluation and treatment, I could not help but return Dr. Reed's smile. He was a wonderful and very talented neurologist who took excellent care of his patients, including new patients like Sam. I hurriedly summarized the situation.

"Eighteen-year-old male who presented with a mild headache. Completely normal neuro exam. Discs flat," I said, referring to the lack of swelling at the optic nerves. "No nuchal rigidity, Kernig's or Brudzinski's sign," I continued, referring to the lack of neck stiffness. "Vitals were slightly elevated on arrival with minimal change at this point. WBC twelve thousand, five hundred with a left shift. CT scan normal except for the possibility of slightly increased density of CSF. LP done without complications and tubes sent to the lab. Initial antibiotics started before going to CT."

"Excellent!" Dr. Reed responded. "I will push the lab to get results from the tap ASAP. On my way over, I called for an ICU bed so we can get him upstairs as soon as it's available."

With perfect timing Ericka briefly stuck her head inside Room 1. "Bed's ready! And I was able to connect with his family. They are en route to the hospital."

"Let's go before his condition deteriorates further," Jay said to Linda, who unlocked the brakes on the stretcher and started pushing it toward the door, where Dr. Reed helped guide it around the corner and toward the elevator that led to the ICU.

Having handed off Sam's care to Dr. Reed, I headed to the nursing desk to see how many patients had come in while I had been with Sam. Thankfully, there were only a few, none of whom had complaints that suggested acute, serious illness.

The day wore on with a steady but manageable stream of patients. When my shift ended, I headed upstairs to the ICU to check on Sam. Dr. Reed happened to be there.

"I'm sure glad you got his antibiotics on board so swiftly," Dr. Reed said as he wrote in Sam's chart. "He crashed in less than an hour of getting him into an ICU bed. He became septic with his pressure abruptly dropping, requiring fluids and vasopressors. We had to sedate him because of his agitation and confusion."

"The lab identified *Neisseria meningitidis,"* he continued as he looked up. "Very nasty bug. He's lucky to be alive." He paused for a moment and then asked me a question.

"So what made you jump on him so quickly?" he asked. "I read the nursing notes and didn't see anything to initially suggest meningitis."

While I had given Dr. Reed the verbal summary of Sam's case when he was in the ER, all of my documentation had not made it upstairs yet to go with the rest of Sam's chart.

I recognized that in the verbal summary, I had left out the one piece of information that had tipped the scales of concern for me. I looked at Sam as he lay in the ICU bed, asleep from the sedative meds he had been given. Both of his feet were under the blankets. I walked toward Sam's left leg and uncovered his foot.

"He had a single petechia on his left great toe," I said as I looked down at Sam's foot.

Jay stopped writing in the chart and turned toward me.

"You're kidding, right?" he asked doubtfully, wondering if I were pulling his leg.

"Look for yourself," I said as I more closely inspected Sam's left foot. Not surprisingly, he now had a few more petechiae on his foot and toes in addition to the one on his great toe. *Neisseria meningitidis*, the bacteria causing Sam's meningitis, is one of the organisms known for creating petechiae.

"Impressive finding," Jay said as he leaned over and peered at Sam's big toe. Without straightening up, he tilted his face upward and said with a twinkle in his eye, "Perhaps I should start referring to you as Dr. Holmes. Dr. Sherlock Holmes." He grinned broadly.

I couldn't help but return his smile. Jay didn't know it, but I had been a fan of Sherlock Holmes since I was a teenager. Later in life, I discovered that the stories about Mr. Holmes' astute observations and seemingly infallible conclusions were actually inspired by a physician, Dr. Joseph Bell, who exhibited similar yet less dramatic skills than the famous detective in Sir Arthur Conan Doyle's fictional writings.

I had no illusion of being in the same galaxy with someone of Dr. Bell's abilities, much less the fictional character Sherlock Holmes, but I enjoyed the reference to the logical and analytical process of searching for clues and making deductions. It's a process all physicians utilize, but in the dynamic and unstable environment of the emergency department, its importance can be significantly magnified.

Sam's medical course for the next seventy-two hours was tumultuous. But the antibiotics, excellent nursing care, and Dr. Reed's knowledge and experience carried Sam through the life-threatening situation. Despite the fact that Sam's life teetered on the edge once or twice during that time, he made it through.

Sam then continued to improve and fully recovered without any permanent deficits or sequelae—a remarkable and wonderful outcome. He went home with all the same personality, qualities, and abilities he had before he became ill.

Of course, incredible challenges like Sam's illness can add another dimension to how we see things in life. I could not help but wonder how Sam might respond if one of his friends complained to him of a headache. I smiled as I visualized Sam suggesting to his friend that he should take off his socks to be sure he didn't have any purple dots on his toes…

What Are You Doing?

Hospitals function differently at night than during the day. There are many reasons for that, but staffing is one of them.

In many community hospitals during the 1980s through the early 2000s, the only physicians routinely present in the hospital throughout the night were ER physicians. Since they were already in the ER seeing patients, they might be called upon to go to other areas of the hospital when an unexpected patient crisis arose, providing emergency care until the patient's regular physician arrived.

Of course, at times, other physicians might be called into the hospital during the night to provide ongoing care for patients who were emergently admitted from the ER into the hospital, sometimes even requiring emergency surgery. And, certainly, obstetricians would appear when babies decided it was their time to come into the world.

The system typically worked well, allowing most physicians to get their needed rest in order to see patients in the office the next day or perform operations in the OR during the daytime. Clearly, one would not wish to have a physician operating on them or making significant health care decisions when they were sleep-deprived.

In the last couple of decades, more hospitals have employed "hospitalists"—doctors who care for many of the patients admitted to the hospital. They work shifts similar to the way ER physicians do—both day and night shifts. That can facilitate care for hospitalized patients and ease the burden on physicians with office-based practices.

For ER physicians, getting called to other areas of the hospital for sudden crises during the day or night can put them in a difficult position. Their first responsibility is to care for patients already in the emergency room and those entering the ER. If there is a critically ill patient in the ER, they cannot leave that patient to go care for another patient in a different area of the hospital. But whenever possible, they try to help.

It was a very late evening in November when a call came to the ER from the surgical floor upstairs, requesting immediate physician assistance for a critically ill patient. Stella, the night ER secretary, hurriedly came to the room where I was seeing a patient and informed me of the urgent request.

I quickly excused myself and rapidly headed to the nurses' station in the ER, mentally reviewing each of the eight patients in the emergency room at that time, satisfying myself they were all stable. Along the way, I asked one of the nurses to stride alongside me as I verbally gave her several orders to carry out on patients while I would be upstairs.

At the nursing station, I hastily glanced through the charts in the rack for patients waiting to be seen, assessing whether any had the likelihood of an acute, serious illness. There were none. I knew that if a critically ill or injured patient did present to the ER during my absence, they would immediately page me overhead to return to the ER.

I ran out of the ER and toward a stairwell along the main hospital corridor. Having already burned about forty seconds ensuring the stability of my patients before leaving the ED, I couldn't wait for the elevators. I did not know what I would encounter upstairs or how long I might be there.

Responding to an in-house emergency was always a little gut-wrenching for me. While I had been well trained to care for people presenting to the ER with all kinds of acute injuries and illnesses, it was different for patients already in the hospital. If it was a cardiac arrest, or a patient who needed to be intubated, or a host of other things we often address in the ER, then it was not anxiety producing.

Sometimes, however, the crisis was related to a procedure or treatment that had taken place earlier in the day, sometimes only an hour or two after its completion. If information about that activity had not made it to the patient's chart, it could substantially limit one's ability to adequately and appropriately address the issue in rapid fashion.

I reached the door to the stairwell and began running up three flights of stairs taking two steps at a time. I opened the door to the third-floor surgical unit, stepped through, and looked both ways down the hall to see which direction I needed to go.

I readily saw my destination. At one end of the corridor, there was a white light blinking above the doorway of the patient's room with two nurses standing there waving me in their direction. *Oooh, this doesn't look good,* I thought as I started running down the hallway.

As I reached the room and started to go in, I asked the two nurses at the door, "What's the story?" This was always the key.

Too often in these situations, the floor nurse caring for the patient is not their "usual" nurse so they're unfamiliar with the patient's problems, or they just came on shift a short time before and hadn't yet "rounded" to assess all their patients. That typically meant there was a paucity of information to share, leaving the responding physician to temporarily fly blind.

Unfortunately, that was the case with this critically ill patient. One nurse's response to my question as I walked past her into the room was, "He's having difficulty breathing!" While it was a good attempt to be helpful, that problem could readily be seen, even in the darkened room illuminated by only a single lamp in the corner.

My immediate response as I went to the patient's bedside was a series of questions for which I needed answers. "Does he have a history of difficulty breathing? How long has this been going on? What is he in the hospital for? Does he have known allergies? What meds has he recently been given?"

I needed prompt answers to all of those questions in order to quickly narrow down the possibilities for his respiratory distress. Often, when patients have significant difficulty breathing, they can't talk because they are so short of breath. One has to get the important information from another source.

It was a bad sign when I heard no response from the nurse in the room and saw from the corner of my eye her flipping through the patient's thick chart that had just been given to her by another person entering the room.

I shifted my complete attention to the patient. "Light, please!" I said loud enough for the room to hear but not so loudly as to frighten the patient in the bed before me. Even in the low light, it was easy to tell the man was indeed in extremis. He was working very hard to breathe but moving very little air.

He lay in bed, the head end of which was elevated about thirty degrees, his arms lying at his side. He was staring straight ahead not responding to my presence—as if he was completely focused on breathing. His eyes were open very wide. His skin was diaphoretic and dusky appearing, noticeable even in the low light. I felt for a radial pulse as I knelt next to him, finding it and noting it was rapid.

He appeared to be in his fifties. He was medium height and medium build with dark hair. He had a large bandage over the front of his neck—clearly the location of recent surgery, the specific kind of which I still did not know as they continued to look through his chart.

I pulled out my stethoscope and quickly listened to both lung fields as he lay in the bed. He was not moving much air, but I could hear upper airway noise, suggesting he had some manner of obstruction in his larger airways. I had noticed earlier his oxygen saturation reading, which was well below normal, despite the high flow of oxygen being administered.

Finally, someone found the light switch for a portion of the overhead lights. The additional light confirmed all that I had seen in the lesser light.

"I need information, ladies!" I said, referring to all of my prior questions. "What surgery did he have and when was it completed?" I could hear more frantic page turning through the chart. I continued my exam as they searched.

"He had surgery on his thyroid this afternoon. He came upstairs around six o'clock," the nurse with the chart said. "He has no allergies. His past medical history is for gout, arthritis, and kidney stones."

"Excellent! Thank you," I said without taking my eyes off the patient.

While the information was good to have, I had already mentally moved beyond that. There were no visible signs of allergic reaction and no swelling of his face or mouth. Two likely causes for his difficulty breathing came to mind: (1) swelling inside his airway that partially obstructed his breathing passage, perhaps due to a difficult intubation prior to his surgery; or (2) bleeding around his airway from his surgery, compressing his airway from the outside. The thyroid gland lies in front of the trachea (windpipe) and is very vascular, containing lots of blood vessels. Surgery in that area has the potential to create substantial bleeding.

Audrey, the respiratory therapist, now rushed into the room and immediately went to the head of the bed. "What's up, Dr. Grant?" she asked in a calm voice as she began setting up things we might need to rapidly employ.

"Audrey, I may need to intubate our patient. Can you set me up?" I knew that if that turned out to be the case, it would be difficult. In this type of situation, there could be swelling on the inside of the airway that would make finding the proper location to insert the tube very challenging.

"Will do, Dr. Grant. Seven and a half? Mac three?" The numbers she asked about were for the size of the endotracheal tube and the type of laryngoscope blade I would use. Since we had worked together often in the ER, she knew what I would use in this situation.

"Sounds good. First, however, I'm going to remove his bandage and see what we've got underneath." I had already begun to peel off the bandage that had been taped down pretty securely. I was able to get it off and was surprised by what I saw.

"Does anyone have a flashlight?" I asked. A nurse at the end of the bed instantly turned on a powerful light, which she directed toward our patient's neck.

He had a horizontal incision in his neck that had been closed with staples. That skin incision was now centered in an area of substantial swelling in his neck. The skin was noticeably stretched over the swollen area. He looked like he had a bullfrog's neck.

I palpated it to determine its consistency. It was firm, not spongy like one might expect if there was air in the soft tissue.

It was clear that he had formed a very large blood clot in his neck post-operatively, concealed by the big, bulky bandage. No doubt that was the source of his airway compromise and difficulty breathing.

"Do you have a staple removal kit?" I asked the nursing staff as soon as I saw his incision area, hoping someone might have placed one in the room, just in case it was needed.

"Not here, Doctor. We'll see if we can find one," someone answered behind me, after which I heard them rush out of the room.

I knew we couldn't wait. His respiratory distress was too severe and had been going on for too long. Despite the oxygen he was being given, the oxygen content in his bloodstream was too low to adequately support his brain function. At age fifty, I also worried about how it would impact the function of his heart, knowing it could lead to irregular heartbeats or possibly even cardiac arrest at any moment.

"Anyone have a needle holder or a straight hemostat?" I asked as I pulled one from my own pocket, my eyes remaining fixed on the patient's neck along with the rapid, shallow rise and fall of his chest. He continued to stare straight ahead, eyes wide open, profusely sweating.

"Yes," Audrey responded, promptly handing me one. While not optimal, I began using the two instruments to bend back the ends of the staples and remove them.

When the first one came out, I knew we were on the right track. They were like buttons on a shirt too tight for the size of belly it covered. After the first button is undone, there is suddenly a gaping hole. The same happened to our patient's skin.

I quickly removed several more. Once the fourth and fifth staple had been taken out, our patient's breathing audibly improved. His color began to pink up as his O2 saturation reading jumped into the low nineties. His respiratory rate slightly improved. I removed two more staples, leaving a large, gaping wound in the man's neck, the skin having retracted to the sides with a large, firm blood clot sitting within the area of opened skin.

I worried he might start bleeding briskly if he moved around too much or became agitated. The skin previously stapled closed had been acting as a compressive force to slow the bleeding. I put my hand on his shoulder just in case I might need to hold him down or grab his hand if he reflexively reached for the open wound on his neck.

I dared not touch the clot. We had temporarily fixed his breathing difficulty. With that crisis now over, I did not wish to create another. Disturbing the clot could start brisk bleeding, which we were not in a position to address in a room with low light and without the necessary instruments or personnel. I carefully covered the open wound with a sterile paper sheet.

"Sir, how are you feeling?" I asked, wanting to see if our patient's brain was functioning well enough to respond while also assessing the quality of his voice. Just because we fixed the "outside" issue related to his airway didn't mean there wasn't an "inside" issue also.

Although he didn't speak, he nodded his head in affirmation. I took that as a very good sign. Clearly, he was doing better and able to now process information.

"Let's get an EKG on our patient," I said, recognizing he had just gone through a very challenging stress test. I wanted to be certain he hadn't developed another problem during the time his oxygenation had been inadequate.

"Audrey, let's keep him on humidified oxygen by mask," I said as Audrey nodded in affirmation.

Our patient's color had now returned to normal, along with his O2 saturation readings. His perspiration was decreasing, and his heart rate was slowing although not yet back to the normal range. He was starting to look about the room without turning his head much, clearly aware of his surroundings. He tilted his head slightly toward me and whispered, "Thank you," and managed a slight smile. Apparently, his brain had been getting enough oxygen to be able to process some of what had just transpired.

His voice, while a little hoarse, didn't suggest evidence of a compromised airway internally. And with all of the other parameters improving, I felt as though we had adequately addressed the underlying cause of the crisis.

I lifted the sterile sheet off his open neck wound to check if any additional bleeding had developed. Thankfully, the wound and clot appeared unchanged. As I began to consider next steps in our patient's care, there was a sudden, loud, agitated voice that boomed from the doorway.

"What are you doing to *my* patient?" Without moving from the bedside, I turned my head to glance at the doorway where I saw a large body silhouetted against the lights in the hallway, hands lifted up and resting on the top of the doorframe, legs spread apart. He looked like a WWE wrestler standing at the edge of the arena, about to enter.

However, there were too many people and too much equipment crowded into the room for him to easily make his way to the patient's bedside. A couple of the nurses had apparently slipped out the door when they saw him approaching, perhaps anticipating a brewing storm.

Even before I looked toward the silhouetted body, I recognized the voice—Dr. Harold Sumpter. Physically, he was a very large person who also happened to be a surgeon. At times, he might intimidate people, intentionally or not, with his physical size or his loud voice. He was a bit of a blowhard and some perceived him as arrogant, but I viewed him more as a breezy day than a tornado.

The tone of Harold's voice combined with its amplitude clearly indicated he was not happy that someone had provided care to *his* patient without *his* approval. Harold sometimes felt others were not capable of providing the quality of care he believed he did, assuming, of course, that he was actually present to provide the care. While the nurses had clearly recognized the patient's critical status earlier, Harold had not yet accepted that assessment.

As usual, Harold's presence and gruff question were intended to challenge what we had done in his absence, creating a palpable tension in the room. It was for that reason the two nurses had disappeared upon his arrival. Harold was known for occasionally throwing a temper tantrum that was not pleasant to endure. The nurses still present were frozen in place, not desiring to speak a word in case they might invoke his displeasure.

Satisfied *our* patient was now stable and the life-threatening crisis averted, I felt like my work was done. After all, I had an emergency room full of patients who also needed my attention.

With Harold's arrival, he could now determine next steps. Clearly, the large clot in the patient's neck that had nearly strangled him was from blood vessels that needed to be tied off or cauterized. Sometimes, despite the surgeon's best efforts in the initial surgery, there might be persistent oozing. Harold would need to take him back to the operating room to address that. It was just a question of when.

I placed the sterile drape back over the neck wound and got up from where I had been kneeling next to the bed.

"Excellent work, ladies," I said as I looked at Audrey and the nurses still in the room. "Thank you for recognizing our patient's critical condition and helping to resolve it quickly."

I then turned and made my way to the door, where I stopped in front of Harold, looking straight into his big, scowling face, as he filled the doorway, his arms still raised above the doorframe, exaggerating his size. I knew he was expecting some sort of apology or offer of regret for having "undone" some of his surgical work before he would step aside to let me pass.

Instead, I reached up with my right hand that held the two bloody hemostats I had just used and slipped them into the shirt pocket of his scrubs, leaning forward to softly answer his question in a voice only he could hear—but hear clearly.

"Saving *our* patient's life..."

I turned sideways as I slipped between Harold's right side and the doorframe, exiting the room.

I smiled as I walked down the hallway toward the elevators, knowing we had averted a terrible post-operative catastrophe for the patient and his family. But I must confess, a small portion of that smile was also because I knew Harold was trying hard to come up with a response to my answer, one that would allow him to maintain his disapproving perspective despite our timely intervention.

The continued silence behind me suggested he either recognized the good work we all had collectively done or his efforts to come up with a retort had failed. While I hoped for the former, I imagined the latter was more likely.

In any case, as I headed back downstairs, I knew the patient appreciated the interim care he had received from the nurses, respiratory therapist, and an ER doc responding to a call for help.

Priorities

"Dr. Grant, this is Medic 4. We have a nineteen-year-old male involved in a car accident." The paramedic on the EMS radio was breathing hard as he delivered his verbal report. I knew what that meant. They had a seriously injured patient, and they were moving as fast as they could to get him to the hospital ER, where I was currently on shift.

No doubt they had taken the "load and go" approach, extricating the patient from the vehicle, loading him into the ambulance as rapidly as possible, and trying to initiate what treatment they could while racing to the hospital.

Many times, critical trauma patients need blood transfusions, which can't be done in the field. Delaying the opportunity to receive blood can mean the difference between life and death. The paramedics and EMTs knew this, which is why they made the important decision to move quickly.

The voice on the radio continued. "The patient was an unrestrained back-seat passenger. He had a pulse on scene but currently has none. CPR is in progress." There was a momentary pause. "And, Doc, every time we do a chest compression, a stream of blood shoots out of a wound in his upper left chest. It seems he was impaled by something, but we don't know what. At your location in one to two minutes."

"Copy, Medic 4. If you are able, apply firm pressure to the wound to diminish his blood loss. Medical Center out." I hung up the EMS radio phone and headed to the nurses' station, relating the information to them so they could begin preparation of the major trauma resuscitation room as rapidly as possible.

"Jane, call the lab and tell them we need two units of type O negative blood *stat.* Also, get a portable X-ray unit over here to stage in the hallway. And call Andy Parks, the chest surgeon, and the OR team—tell them we need them right away." Jane, our exceedingly competent ER secretary, nodded her head as she was already dialing numbers.

I stuck my head inside Major Trauma Room 4, where the nurses and respiratory techs were hastily preparing the trays, instruments, tubes for blood draw, oxygen tubing, and other items that would be needed upon the patient's arrival.

"We'll need an SMA 12, CBC, PT/PTT, tox screen, type and cross for four units of blood, and three fourteen-gauge IVs as soon as you can get them in. Hang one bag of Ringer's lactate and the other two normal saline."

These were the blood tests we needed and the type of IV fluids we would use until we could get the blood transfusion going, assuming there was a real possibility the patient might survive.

"And please get out a thoracotomy tray." This was a sterile metal tray containing a host of metal instruments used to surgically cut open a person's chest in rapid fashion. I hoped we wouldn't need it, but it was wise to have it readily available.

Just as I finished the verbal instructions, the ambulance roared into the emergency entrance, its lights flashing, visible through the glass double doors. The paramedics and EMTs hurriedly unloaded the patient from the back of the ambulance and came through the doorway. One medic was performing CPR as the stretcher was rolling. One was using a BVM to try to breathe for the patient, holding the mask over his mouth and squeezing the bag. A cervical collar, a firm plastic stabilizing device, was around the patient's neck to keep his head and neck immobilized as he lay on a wooden backboard on the stretcher.

Two other medics were pushing the stretcher, one of whom was carrying the heavy cardiac monitor/defibrillator that had wire leads attached to the patient. They had been able to initiate a lot of treatment and monitoring in the very short time it took to get to the hospital. The fact they were all drenched in sweat spoke to their effort. They were incredibly talented and dedicated men and women.

As the stretcher and mass of people squeezed through the double doors, one of the EMTs who had been holding a pressure dressing over the young man's left upper chest had to step away from the patient as the rest of the team came through. In doing so, the pressure dressing fell away from the wound.

The enormity of the injury became readily apparent when the next chest compression ejected a thick column of blood upward about three inches above the patient's chest, after which it rained down onto the stretcher and the floor underneath.

In only a matter of seconds, they traversed the hallway and wheeled the patient into Major Trauma Room 4.

A quick visual assessment revealed a teenage male who was about five ten to six feet tall, weighing about 180 pounds, with an athletic build. He was unconscious and unresponsive, diaphoretic (sweaty), pale but with a slight tinge of skin color. There were no grossly visible injuries or deformities except for the wound just below his left collarbone, where the blood had been pouring out.

I grabbed a package of sterile four-by-four-inch gauze sponges and placed them over the wound just under his left clavicle.

"Hold very firm pressure on the wound," I said to David, the paramedic standing next to me, pushing my hand down on top of his against the patient's chest to demonstrate the degree of force needed.

In one coordinated, quick movement with hands inserted into the openings on the backboard, the team of providers moved the critically ill patient from the EMS stretcher to the hospital stretcher.

Immediately, two of the EMTs exited the room with the EMS stretcher and all their equipment on it, making room for everyone else who needed to participate in the care of the patient.

Joe, the respiratory therapist, hurriedly connected the oxygen tubing to the wall plug and continued bagging the young man. Eva, one of the ER nurses, connected the EKG leads that had been attached to the ambulance monitor to the cable running to the ER monitor over the patient's bed.

During the transition, Mark, the lead paramedic at the foot of the stretcher, continued his verbal report: "Doc, there was substantial damage to the vehicle, and the driver and front-seat passenger were dead on scene. None of the occupants had their seat belts on." The information he conveyed was important in assessing the degree of potential injuries the patient might have suffered.

Mark caught his breath and continued, "We could not determine what object had impaled the patient who was in the back seat. He was unconscious and unresponsive on our arrival but did have a very thready pulse. By the time we got him extricated from the vehicle, he had lost his pulse. There was substantial blood loss at the scene and during transport."

As Mark was providing the important scene information, I was at the patient's right side quickly conducting a trauma exam using my eyes, ears (via stethoscope), and hands to search for evidence of injury. It was important to begin with an assessment of the patient's airway, breathing, and circulation as the initial facet of an inclusive head-to-toe exam, prioritizing for treatment the identified injuries. One must be careful to avoid distraction by gruesome-appearing injuries that are not life-threatening until one has searched for and identified true life threats.

When examining the patient's chest, I listened carefully to his breath sounds, which surprisingly were present on both sides, suggesting that the hole in his upper left chest may not have actually entered the chest cavity where it could have collapsed his left lung. That probably meant the injury was to a large blood vessel outside the chest cavity that supplied blood to his left arm, known as the subclavian artery or vein—or both. Because of their size, if punctured or torn, the patient could rapidly bleed to death.

"Hold CPR," I said as I glanced up at the heart monitor and saw a rapid heart rate of about 160 with normal complexes, simultaneously feeling for a femoral pulse in the patient's groin area.

"No pulse," I announced. "Continue CPR." Billy, one of the paramedics, resumed the CPR he had been doing on the patient since his arrival. He, like the other EMTs and paramedics, was drenched in sweat from the intensive physical effort.

The nurses had already drawn blood for lab tests and were now starting the IVs. Joe, the respiratory therapist, had set out the equipment necessary to intubate the patient, so I moved quickly to the head of the stretcher and performed what was thankfully an uncomplicated intubation. That now made it easier to oxygenate and ventilate the patient while also protecting his airway from fluids that might come up from his stomach.

There were two simultaneous "IV in!" statements. I asked the nurses and paramedics to squeeze the IV bags as much as they could, trying to force fluids into the patient's blood vessels in an effort to raise his blood pressure. At the moment, it was so low it couldn't be detected, but his heart rhythm showed his heart was electrically working as fast as possible.

Lab personnel entered the room with the two units of type O negative blood, which I asked the nurses to administer through the IVs attached to the bags of normal saline solution.

From the initial trauma exam, the only obvious life-threatening injury was the puncture wound below the patient's left clavicle. It was also possible he had a closed head injury, but there was no substantial bruising, swelling, or palpable skull or facial fractures. It would be hard to tell about his brain function until we got his blood pressure up to where it could better perfuse his brain and subsequently scan it when he was stable.

I moved back to the upper chest wound and tried to assess it better. While maintaining pressure to diminish the bleeding as best I could, I felt around the wound for any firm objects that might be embedded. There were none.

I palpated the length of his clavicle to see if perhaps it had broken and been pushed inward and downward to lacerate the subclavian vessel in its close proximity. The clavicle was intact.

I again instructed the paramedic to hold firm pressure on the wound as I called out for X-ray to come into the room and set up for a chest X-ray, along with a quick X-ray of his cervical spine (neck), searching for other possible injuries.

As they moved their large, heavy equipment into the room, I reassessed the amount of fluid and blood we had given our patient. He had two liters of IV fluid and one unit of blood already in him. I asked the paramedic performing CPR to hold his chest compressions as I felt again for a femoral pulse.

To my delight—and amazement—he had a pulse! Our patient, whose name we learned was William, had a weak, thready femoral pulse. In light of the substantial bleeding he had experienced prior to arrival, generating a palpable pulse at this point in his care was a significant accomplishment by the team. It meant that the rapid, coordinated effort had improved William's chance of survival.

"Femoral pulse present," I said. "Hold CPR and let's try to get a blood pressure. X-ray, please get our images ASAP."

As the techs positioned the X-ray plates for the images, Eva spoke out. "BP sixty-four over forty," she said with a smile on her face. After shooting the X-rays with the team briefly out of the room, the tech rapidly left to get them developed and back to us.

As the tech was leaving, Dr. Andy Parks came in. He was a slender man who stood a little over six feet tall. He always had a calm composure and never got overly excited, agitated, or impatient. He was cool under fire, in part because he had served as a surgeon in the Vietnam War. He had seen and operated on a lot of horrendous injuries during his service.

"What ya got?" Andy asked in his low-key manner as he came up to the opposite side of the stretcher, his hands in the pockets of his white coat that covered his surgical scrubs, his eyes sweeping up and down the patient who lay before him.

"Nineteen-year-old male involved in a high-energy MVC. He was a passenger in the back seat, no seat belt. Driver and front-seat passenger DOA. He seems to have been impaled upon something and appears to have a lacerated subclavian vessel. He had a pulse at the scene but lost it en route. He has had a sinus tachycardia the whole time, now with a BP of sixty-four over forty. He has lost a lot of blood, which we're trying to replace with O negative blood and IV fluids, attempting to get him out of hemorrhagic shock."

As Andy looked at the blood and fluids hanging on the IV poles, I continued. "We've got two units of O negative blood almost in, with four units of typed-and-crossed blood on the way." I took a quick breath.

"Grossly, I don't find any significant injuries except for the wound below his left clavicle. He has no palpable fractures and his abdomen is soft. He's intubated. Chest and C-spine X-rays on the way. Initial blood work should be back any minute. Don't know his neurologic status since he's been in shock, but no significant evidence of blunt head trauma."

As I finished the update, the radiology tech came in and popped the X-rays up on the view boxes in the trauma room. Andy scanned the chest X-ray while I looked at the three views of the cervical spine, followed by the chest X-ray.

"No visible C-spine injury," I said as I then looked at the chest film. "I don't see any pneumothorax, hemothorax, or pulmonary contusion. ET tube in good position."

"Yes, and I don't see any gross abnormality of his aorta," Andy said as he made his way to the left side of the patient. He and I had worked together on other cases, and we had a good rapport. Again, he never got rattled. He always took a methodical and practical approach.

Andy put on a pair of sterile gloves and spoke to the paramedic holding the pressure dressing against the young man's upper chest. "Let's take that off for a moment."

As soon as he did, blood came pouring out of the wound. Andy instantly inserted his index finger deep into the wound and felt around for a few seconds. The flow of the blood greatly diminished.

"Yep, it feels like he has a hole in his subclavian vessel. We need to get him to the OR." Just as he spoke those words, one of the OR nurses entered the room along with the anesthesiologist.

"BP ninety-six over sixty, heart rate one thirty two. He has a radial pulse," Eva said loudly so all could hear, again with a smile on her face. Several of us smiled with her. We had been able to accomplish what we set out to do—get William out of shock as rapidly as possible and give him a better chance to survive.

Dr. Parks continued to stand next to William, keeping his index finger in the hole in the young man's chest wall as he communicated how he wanted the operating room set up for the surgery he needed to perform.

Jane, our secretary, entered the room and handed me the test results that had just come back from the lab. I read them aloud for Andy and the OR team. "SMA 12 normal. His hemoglobin before the two units of blood was eight." I handed the results to the anesthesiologist.

Andy Parks looked over at me. "Great teamwork, Tom," he said, offering a kind smile. "Looks like we're ready to go to work. Let's take him to the OR. Please tell the lab to send the cross-matched blood to the OR as soon as it's ready." One of the nurses unlocked the brake on the stretcher so it could be rolled.

The OR nurse, anesthesiologist, and a couple of the ER nurses prepared to move the stretcher as soon as Andy Parks was ready to walk alongside them, literally holding his finger in the dike to keep blood from pouring out of William's punctured blood vessel.

As we moved the young man out of the room, both the ER staff and the EMS team felt a great sense of accomplishment. In the span of about thirty-five minutes, we had transformed this young man's condition from undergoing CPR without a pulse to having an adequate blood pressure with his singular injury identified and temporarily addressed. Additionally, his airway had been secured, labs done, X-rays performed and reviewed, blood administered—and the surgeon and OR team were present and now transitioning our patient to the operating room. With incredible teamwork from end to end, we had collectively provided this young man a chance to live again despite exceedingly dire circumstances.

I helped as we wheeled the stretcher out of the major resuscitation room and navigated the first turn toward the operating room across the back hallway outside the emergency department. I let go of the stretcher as I watched them hurriedly exit the ER.

With them went my hope William would survive his tragic accident. Now that my part of the effort was completed, it was time to put aside my elation over the extraordinary teamwork and go see the next patient.

I looked down at my scrubs, recognizing for the first time they were covered in blood. I knew I would need to change into the extra pair I kept in our office before seeing other patients.

As I was about to turn and go change, I looked up and noticed a woman who appeared to be in her late twenties or early thirties dressed in a business suit standing outside Room 12, about fifteen feet down the hall in front of me. Her hands were on her hips, her legs spread apart a foot or so, and her head slightly tilted to one side with a frustrated look on her face.

Odd, I thought as I wondered what, and to whom, she was attempting to communicate with her body language. Was she appalled by all the blood on my scrubs? Or was there someone or something behind me that I hadn't noticed as I came out of the trauma room. I turned my head to look, thinking perhaps a child or relative of hers had left the room she was in without her permission. She seemed to be irritated about something.

I looked back at the woman. She had not moved a muscle or changed the look of disdain on her face. I started to speak, wanting to inquire if there was something I could help her with, but she spoke first.

"I came in before he did," she forcefully said as she looked directly at me with her hands still on her hips. For a moment, I was confused—was she somehow connected to the accident? What was she trying to convey? She abruptly clarified it for me.

"I've been waiting here forty minutes," she said, now shifting her head straight up. "And I came in before he did. I saw them bring him down the hallway."

Although I heard her words, I felt as though I had failed to grasp what she was trying to tell me. Surely, she didn't mean what she just said.

She maintained her stance, waiting for a response. After my mind quickly replayed her words several times, it concluded the information was indeed accurate. She did say what I couldn't believe she had the heartless audacity to say.

As she had said, she witnessed the young man come in on a stretcher, multiple paramedics pushing it with the ambulance lights flashing brightly behind the automatic glass doors through which they had brought him. She had also seen one of the paramedics performing CPR, pumping his chest as they hastily moved him down the hallway and into the resuscitation room.

And she had seen the column of blood spurting up from his chest with each downward compression, evidence of which was clearly visible in my blood-stained scrubs, now before her very eyes.

I could feel anger growing in my mind. Two options for responding to her words flashed through my head.

The first was to confront her incredibly uncaring and self-centered remark. That was promptly followed by a desire to just turn and walk away. But I rapidly compromised, recognizing that this person needed to grasp a firmer understanding of where she was and how things worked.

I paused, wanting to speak in an even tone of voice, devoid of the incredible degree of emotion roaring through my brain at this juncture in time.

"Ma'am, this is an emergency room. We don't see people based on the time they check in. We see people based on how sick or how injured they are." I hesitated, wanting those words to sink in, and hoping there might be some degree of remorse about her comment. But there appeared to be none. She maintained her stance, just tilting her head slightly to the other side as if my answer was not sufficient for her and she was waiting for more.

I complied. "The teenager you saw come into the ER covered in blood and near death now has a chance to live as they begin operating on him." I stood there, letting that sink in also before I continued, hoping it might actually cause her to think about what she was saying.

"After I go change my scrubs, I will check to see which other patients, in addition to you, have been waiting to be seen, and then I will care for them in the order of the severity of their condition."

I did not wait for a response from her—verbal or otherwise. I turned and walked down the hallway toward the small physicians' office.

I felt assured she would file a complaint with administration and I would hear from them. Certainly, she would not provide all the facts. I knew her emphasis would be that she had to wait to be seen. I also thought she might decide to leave before I saw her since she wasn't receiving the speedy treatment she desired. But that's not how it unfolded.

Once my scrubs were changed, I checked the waiting charts. There were only two—the woman in Room 12 whose chief complaint was an "ankle injury" and an older patient in Room 13 with a complaint of "leg pain." Not knowing the basis for the man's leg pain, I went to see him first, after which I headed to her room.

She had at least returned to the stretcher in the room, on which she was now seated when I entered. I introduced myself and sat down on the stool in front of her. Normally, I would apologize for the wait, but in this case, I didn't feel it was necessary. She knew very well the reason for her wait.

"Now, what sort of problem can we help you with this evening, Ms. Finley?" I asked as I looked her squarely in the eyes. She didn't look away.

"My ankle hurts," was her curt response. I waited just a tad to see if I would get any additional information, or if she was going to make me draw out every necessary detail.

"Did you injure it?" I asked.

"Yes," was all she offered. I could feel her restrained anger, but I struggled to understand the basis for it.

"How about describing the manner in which you injured it—what you were doing at the time, and what physically happened to your ankle." I wanted to try to get some useful information to determine how to approach her exam.

"I stepped off the curb." Her passive-aggressive attitude continued. I had no intention of engaging in a confrontation with her, which she may have been looking for—I wasn't sure. I stayed on the standard approach to obtaining a history and physical.

I continued to draw out the details of her "accident," which amounted to only a mild twisting of her ankle without a fall or any other injuries. Her exam showed no swelling and minimal tenderness over the outer ankle bone (the fibula). Clearly, this was a pretty minor injury.

"And how long ago did this happen?" I asked.

Interestingly, that question resulted in a change in her body language. She put both hands down on the stretcher, straightened her arms, and then looked down to the ground. She hesitated before providing an answer.

"Three days ago," was her softly spoken response.

In my mind, I hoped that shift in posture meant she might have finally come to grips with her uncaring and egocentric complaint of not being seen before the dying young man.

I sent her off to X-ray, wanting to be sure I didn't miss anything such as a hairline fracture or some other injury that might need to be treated with something other than an ACE wrap, elevation of the ankle when sitting, ambulation as tolerated, Tylenol as needed, and the tincture of time. As I suspected, the X-ray was negative. She was discharged home without further incident.

Despite her departure from the ER, her words and her attitude continued to plague my mind for weeks afterward. I struggled to accept there were people who could have such a perspective. It was unfathomable. I just couldn't process it.

I tried to imagine a possible basis for her outlook. Perhaps she had experienced a number of very difficult or disappointing circumstances in the days or weeks leading up to that evening's ER visit, and her frame of mind had temporarily become twisted in the midst of her pain.

Or perhaps her life to that point had been filled with hardship, frustration, inequities, misfortune, and despondency. Maybe she had suffered through some tragic circumstances earlier in her life with which she continued to struggle.

Still, it was hard for me to grasp how a person could demonstrate no empathy or compassion for a dying young man seen with one's own eyes, and instead place the desire for quick treatment of a minor three-day-old injury above the saving of a human life. It was beyond my ability to comprehend.

Over time, my frustration and disappointment began to transform into great sorrow for her. The anger she carried had to be a tremendous burden, devastating her life.

I began to hope she would find someone in her life who demonstrated true love and selflessness for others—a living example who could help heal her wounds and return happiness to her life.

That thought led me to reflect upon some of the wonderful people I have encountered in life and in the ER. I have been encouraged by the amazing love, caring, and compassion I have seen in many folks who live that true love for one another—even to strangers. I hoped she would have that opportunity as well.

~ ~ ~

In casual conversations with people, if they learn I'm a physician in emergency medicine, they often comment about how such a job must be terribly stressful, having to make critical, life-impacting decisions at a moment's notice and dealing with so many difficult situations.

I usually acknowledge that certain cases can be very challenging and demand every bit of knowledge and skill one has acquired over time. However, if one has been fortunate to be well trained in an emergency medicine program, the pressure of caring for critically ill patients isn't the greatest strain.

The most stressful aspect of the job can often be dealing with people like Ms. Finley, whose demands are without regard for others and centered solely upon one's self. While her perspective represents an extreme edge of the spectrum, unfortunately, lesser degrees are too often encountered in the ER—and in life itself.

Unconditional love, although challenging to attain in one's life, is an incredibly powerful medicine that can heal many of the wounds and troubles we encounter in life.

Too Close to Home

I was back in the obstetrics wing of the hospital, making my way down the hallway, my mind in another world.

I had just left the nursery where Dr. Robertson, our family's pediatrician, had conveyed wonderful news to me that I wanted to share with my wife, Jenna, as soon as possible.

In my mind, I could still see Dr. Robertson's smiling face as he looked up from examining our newborn son lying in the bassinet between us, under the warmer. He removed the stethoscope from his ears and offered words I longed to hear: "He's about as perfect as it gets!"

I grinned at Dr. Robertson. "Thanks, Peter. I really appreciate you checking him over so thoroughly."

Dr. Robertson had been our pediatrician for many years. He was smart, kind, experienced, and witty. He loved his patients and cared deeply for their well-being. He was everything you would want in a physician.

His declaration lifted a great burden from my mind.

As a parent, one cannot help but be concerned about the health and well-being of one's child throughout the pregnancy. Even with today's ultrasound technology that allows one to peek into the womb at different times throughout the pregnancy, it can only assess so much about the unborn child's development and condition.

From conception through birth, the seamless coordination of trillions of actions taking place at a molecular level within the mother and unborn child is unbelievably complex yet breathtakingly beautiful.

It's inconceivable to think that we all begin as a single cell, invisible to the naked eye. And that one unique cell becomes trillions upon trillions of cells, each knowing how and when to differentiate into fingers, toes, eyes, ears, heart, lungs, brain, skin, and so many other organs—all of which collectively work together to provide us the opportunity for life in this world. Such life is amazingly resilient yet also incredibly fragile in today's world. It is an amazing phenomenon—truly a gift from God.

As a physician, aware of the many potential yet very infrequent problems that might arise in the development of an unborn child, I could not chase away a remnant of anxiety deep within my thoughts that lingered throughout my wife's pregnancy. I could not help but wonder about what the ultrasound might be missing. Dr. Robertson had just removed that weary load from my mind.

After doing some of the obligatory paperwork, I left Jack, our newborn son, in the capable hands of the nursery staff and headed back toward Jenna's room in the obstetric wing. Soon after delivery, I had been shooed off with Jack to the nursery for his evaluation while Elizabeth, our OB doctor, and the nurses stayed with Jenna.

Although it seemed like only moments had passed since I left Jenna's room, it had actually been about forty-five minutes. I thought about how exhausted she must be, not just from the labor and delivery but also from all the changes her body was rapidly undergoing as it began adjusting its physiology to now support a child living outside her body rather than inside. I expected—and hoped—she would be soundly sleeping.

As I walked down the corridor toward her room at the other end, I was surprised by the absence of people. Normally, there would be nurses moving in and out of the rooms, with one or two moms walking the floor trying to speed up their labor. I imagined there must be lots of activity within the rooms for the hallway to be this empty.

About a third of the way down the hall, I began to hear a melodic dinging sound coming from the nurses' station. I knew it must be an alarm of some type. I wished alarms on the equipment in the ER were as pleasant as the ones I now heard. The ER alarms were all very annoying sounds. Of course, that was by design, making one want to silence them as soon as possible by addressing the underlying issue.

As I passed the nursing desk halfway down the corridor, I saw no one there. I glanced at the array of screens displaying various pieces of information but couldn't easily identify which one was the cause of the pleasant chirping. Multiple lights were flashing in different areas.

I realized I probably wouldn't be able to figure it out before someone arrived and swiftly took care of the concern. Since I had my own special "patient" to see, I continued toward Jenna's room.

I arrived at Room 406 and quietly pushed open the door to see Jenna lying in bed with her eyes closed. I silently entered, closing the door softly behind me. I approached her bedside to sneak a peek at her while she slept, wondering if she had a smile on her face as she dreamed about our second child and what his personality and mannerisms would be like as he grew up.

As I moved closer, I was distracted by a light blinking to the left of Jenna's bed, wondering what it was for. Thankfully, I thought, it wasn't making any noise that might awaken Jenna from her well-deserved slumber.

As I looked more closely, I realized the red blinking light was from her blood pressure monitor. It was flashing the words "NO READING." Usually, that just meant the cuff had come off the patient's arm or had become disconnected. I visually followed the tubing, noting the connections were all intact and that it was still attached to her arm.

That's odd, I thought as a momentary flash of concern appeared in my mind like a single burst from a Roman candle firework going off against a vast, deep, dark sky.

I instinctively hit the "Recycle" button on the BP monitor to have it repeat its inflation of the cuff and the measurement of Jenna's BP, anticipating it would come back in the normal range. But my mind had already shifted from new-dad mode to doctor mode, and I felt the need for immediate confirmation of my assumption.

I put my hand on Jenna's shoulder to gently arouse her from sleep—hating to do so but wanting to be sure she was OK.

"Jen?" I said in a normal tone of voice, expecting her to readily awaken—either from my calling of her name or the now inflating blood pressure cuff as it squeezed her arm. I simultaneously looked at the rise and fall of her chest to determine her breathing pattern, noticing it was shallow and at an increased rate. I then glanced at her right hand, where her fingertips appeared to be a dusky purple in the low light.

That single burst of the Roman candle in my mind now transitioned to multiple bright flashes of light accompanied by thunderous booms.

Jenna did not respond to my gentle effort to awaken her. I now spoke more loudly as I vigorously shook her shoulder. "Jenna, are you OK?"

No response. The blood pressure cuff had begun deflating and once again flashed the words "NO READING." My mind now exploded like a night sky filled with fireworks.

My wife was unresponsive with no measurable blood pressure, fast shallow respirations, and dusky extremities. For a split second, it was hard to grasp. Forty-five minutes earlier, she had been happily celebrating the birth of Jack, and now she was in shock, her life in the balance.

I knew her shock needed immediate treatment, but I had no equipment with which to do it. I hit the nurse call button on the device lying on her bed and then used the bed control to raise the foot end of Jenna's bed higher while lowering the head of her bed as far down as possible. I was trying to invert her position to improve the blood flow to her brain with whatever blood pressure she could generate.

I then searched for Jenna's femoral pulse with my right hand, hoping with all my heart that the other signs of shock were misleading. As I did so, my mind raced through the possibilities as to why her blood pressure was so low.

She hadn't lost a lot of blood during the delivery, although I knew she could be oozing blood into her uterus if it had not contracted down after the birth. There was also the possibility she had received some pain medication that might dilate her blood vessels and lower her blood pressure. My mind added other potential causes to the growing list, but I knew the first two were most likely.

There it was—a very weak femoral pulse, meaning Jenna had a blood pressure of about fifty—less than half of normal, confirming she was in shock. The full weight of that realization immediately fell upon me. Not knowing how long she had been in this state, I realized there was a serious risk of her losing brain, kidney, and other organ function, possibly even her life. Reversing this state as rapidly as possible was critical to her well-being.

I vigorously pinched her thigh, knowing that inducing pain can sometimes create a physiologic response of raising one's blood pressure and heart rate. Simultaneously, I firmly massaged her uterus in her lower abdomen, knowing that if it didn't stay contracted, it would continue to ooze blood into the cavity where the baby had been minutes earlier. Typically, the medication in her IV would help that take place, but it isn't always 100 percent effective.

In the seconds that quickly passed as I carried out these actions, there was no response to the nurse call button. I pushed it again. As I did, my mind instantly replayed the alarms going off at the empty nurses' station I had just walked past. There was no one to alert of Jenna's undetectable blood pressure!

Again, I wondered how long she had been in this condition.

I hit the BP "Recycle" button again, hoping to see some degree of improvement from the interventions, minor as they were. I grabbed pillows and stuffed them under Jenna's legs and buttocks, trying to further upend her position with whatever means I could. I also reached up to the oxygen cannula and slipped it into her nose, turning up the flow of oxygen. Then I returned to vigorously massaging her uterus as I awaited the readout of the BP monitor.

The number sixty now shown in bright-red numbers. At least we were moving in the right direction. But there was no more I could do without equipment. I needed help *immediately*. I still had not received any response from the nursing station via the intercom.

I did not want to leave Jenna, but I needed to.

I turned and ran out of the room and into the hallway, hoping to see nurses and docs who I could call to our assistance. As I turned the corner of her doorway, I looked out at the same long, empty corridor—no one at the nursing station and no one exiting patients' rooms. It was deserted.

I knew it would take me too long to search for the equipment I needed to treat Jenna's shock, and I couldn't just wait for someone to appear.

So I stood in the middle of the hallway outside her door and yelled as loudly as I possibly could, "I need two fourteen-gauge IV catheters and two bags of Ringer's lactate in Room 406 *stat*!"

I knew my voice reached every room along the hallway, penetrating the solid doors to rooms where they were shut.

But to be sure, I yelled again. "And I need them *now…right now*!"

I dashed back into the room and to Jenna's bedside, reinitiating the firm massage of her uterus. I hit the "Recycle" button for the BP cuff and attempted to arouse her. "Jenna? Jenna, are you with me?"

Perhaps it was the pain of my uterine massage rather than my voice that prompted a response, but at least I got a moan from her. While not what I had hoped for, I took it as progress.

In less than a minute from my unorthodox request, two nurses came flying into the room, turning the corner so swiftly they almost slammed into the doorpost. They brought IV fluids, Angiocaths, and tubing in their arms, spilling it all onto the bed alongside Jenna. As I grabbed one IV catheter and opened it to insert it into Jenna's arm, I hurriedly communicated to them she was in shock and unresponsive following her recent delivery.

I asked one of the nurses to continue the uterine massage and the other to start an IV in Jenna's left arm as I began to insert an IV catheter in her right arm. My request probably wasn't needed—they saw the same priorities I did and were on top of it as speedily as I was. I asked if either knew what meds Jenna had been given after delivery, but neither had been her nurse.

Elizabeth, Jenna's obstetrician, then came running into the room just as we connected the IV tubing to the bags and opened up the IV fluids to run as rapidly as possible. I hit the BP "Recycle" button again.

Elizabeth, knowing what had transpired with Jenna while I was in the nursery, immediately put her hand on Jenna's uterus, recognizing it was larger than it should be and not as firm as desired. While I thought I had been doing adequate uterine massage to help stop the bleeding, Elizabeth took it up a couple of levels and began expelling clots from Jenna's uterus onto the white sheets beneath her. Those clots represented significant bleeding and had kept the uterus enlarged, preventing it from fully clamping down after childbirth, leading to further blood loss.

In a matter of seconds, Elizabeth forcefully expelled between one and two units (about three to four cups) of blood onto the bed. Add that to the blood and fluid loss from childbirth, as well as blood loss we had not yet visualized, and it explained why Jenna's blood pressure was so terribly low.

With Elizabeth's presence, one of the nurses dashed off to the lab with a blood specimen to determine Jenna's current blood count. The IV fluids had begun to raise her blood pressure along with the pain from Elizabeth's intense uterine massage, and Jenna began to sluggishly respond. Asked how she was doing, Jenna responded with a weak "OK," followed by moans due to Elizabeth's continued efforts.

After squeezing the IV bags to hurriedly infuse as much fluid as possible into Jenna, her BP reached eighty-two, which under the circumstances was wonderful, although still abnormally low. The blood count soon came back as twenty-eight, meaning Jenna had lost more than a quarter of her blood volume in less than an hour. We knew it would drop further since we had replaced the lost blood with only IV fluids.

Elizabeth increased the medication in Jenna's IV bag to further enhance the muscular tone in her uterus, trying to minimize any additional oozing. The laboratory was preparing blood for an emergency transfusion.

With the treatment that had been rapidly initiated and the improvement in blood pressure, it was now time for watchful waiting. As I stayed at Jenna's bedside, I continued to assess her thinking as the pain medication she had been given after delivery began to wear off. I hoped and prayed there would be no long-term effects from her prolonged hemorrhagic shock.

Once Jenna's blood pressure reached one hundred, we slowly and carefully flattened out the bed rather than keeping her in the head-down position. At that point, we were all able to take a breath, and I thanked Elizabeth and the nurses for their quick response.

I suddenly realized I may have created some significant anxiety or distress for other ladies on the floor who heard me screaming in the hallway. I apologized for my unusual and potentially unsettling request for assistance.

They assured me it was not a concern and expressed their regret for not catching Jenna's condition sooner.

After an hour or two passed, Jenna became more coherent and was able to converse enough for me to conclude she probably didn't suffer any significant long-term brain injury. Over the next few days, we continued to monitor Jenna's blood count, knowing we would need to transfuse her if other symptoms related to her blood loss developed.

Eventually, Jenna's blood count dropped to nineteen. She had lost a little more than half of the blood in her body during and after Jack's birth.

Elizabeth wanted to transfuse her, but Jenna talked her out of it, recognizing that transfusions have both benefits and risks. Jenna wanted to avoid the potential for any additional complications that might prolong her hospital stay.

With her blood count remaining around nineteen after several checks, we felt it had reached its lowest point and would slowly rise from there over the weeks and months to come.

Bringing a child into the world is an amazing and joyous event. Yet it has long been recognized that serious risks also exist with the wonder of childbirth. Modern medicine has decreased those risks but not eliminated them. Thankfully, in Jenna's case, the birth complications were addressed in time to prevent disastrous consequences.

I was thankful that Elizabeth was there to deliver Jack. She was an extremely competent physician who gave me great comfort during and after the delivery process. And the nurses were incredible in their rapid response and compassionate care.

After staying in the hospital for five days, we were able to leave with our newborn bundle of joy, which Jack has continued to be from the day he was born! Thankfully, there have been no other surprises like the one we had on his birthday!

Losing Sight

I hated to start the evening this way. All the rooms were full when I came on shift, and patients were continuing to sign in to the ER. David, who was the doc on the day shift, was finishing up two patients he had seen before I arrived, but the rest were mine—some of whom had signed into the ER more than an hour before my shift even began. So I started far behind.

As always, I first rapidly scanned the nine charts on patients already in rooms but not yet seen. No one appeared to have critically ill complaints or unstable vital signs. There was the usual mix of various pains, fevers, GI complaints, and a few less ordinary concerns. Thankfully, there were only a couple of lacerations, which can require more time than other types of patient encounters.

Another welcome surprise was that one of the patients I thought I was to see was actually waiting on their personal physician to come into the hospital ER to see them. That didn't happen often, but on nights like this, it was certainly appreciated.

I next checked the five charts that had signed in but were still in the waiting room until a bed in the ER became available. Once again, a variety of complaints, but none that required promotion to the front of the line. As always, in the ER the sickest patients need to be seen first. They are unable to wait in line.

The nurses on shift also confirmed they didn't have any patients that appeared critical at the moment.

I grabbed three charts that I knew I could care for quickly and headed to the respective rooms. The first was a knee injury I examined and sent to X-ray. Next was a painful earache, which I was able to examine and write a prescription for, then hand the chart to the nurse for discharge. And the third was a case of the flu—a patient with classic symptoms who didn't need any additional testing, allowing them to be discharged as well.

I felt pretty good, having seen three patients and diagnosed and discharged two of them in the first thirty minutes. I headed back to the nursing desk to drop the charts into the "Orders" box for the nurses to carry out their tasks.

I was abruptly disappointed to note the five charts in the waiting room had grown to eight. I wasn't catching up. I picked up three more charts and headed down the hallway to the rooms near the back of the ER. Unfortunately, these cases would take me a little longer. One was a laceration and another was an eye injury.

As I walked down the hallway on the right side of the ER, there were multiple patients standing at the door to their rooms or next to the curtains that created a partition for their spot in the emergency room. Clearly, everyone was hoping I would be stopping at their room first, and I could hear the exasperation as I hurriedly walked past some of them, heading for rooms further down the hallway.

As rapidly as I could, without diminishing thoroughness, I evaluated the three patients, started their workup and/or treatment, and headed back to the nurses' desk for round three—hoping to not see more charts piling up. Unfortunately, I was disappointed again. More appeared. It was disheartening. At that time in my career, there was no ready backup when the ER resources were stretched to their max. Our group had enough coverage for the various scheduled shifts but not enough to call in an extra doc when it became extra busy.

This time, I picked up four charts and headed down the left hallway. Again, patients were standing at the door of almost every room, even rooms where I had already seen patients. It felt like a very busy Saturday night. Rarely did it get this busy on a Thursday night.

I was about to walk past Rooms 15 and 16, each with a stretcher in the room. These two rooms were separated by a curtain between them. A woman in her thirties was standing at the curtain to Room 15, and an older man in his sixties stood at the far side of Room 16. In my hand, I had charts for Rooms 7, 8, 9, and 13.

I walked past Room 15 as I looked down at the chart for the patient in Room 7, whom I planned to see next. From the corner of my eye, I saw the older man step out of Room 16 and into my path as I was hurrying down the hall.

In that brief moment, my mind silently let out an inaudible *ugh*, anticipating that the man would inquire as to how long it would be before I saw his relative in Room 16. My standard response had to be: "I just don't know. I'm seeing patients as quickly as I can, but if more seriously ill patients arrive, I must see them first. So I just don't know, but I'll do the best I can."

I stopped and looked up from the charts in my hand. I attempted to conceal my frustration at being bumped off course as I was trying my best to be maximally efficient, knowing that people had been waiting longer than usual. I disliked this scenario more than any of my patients. I was certain about that.

The man looked intently into my eyes as he extended his hand toward me and spoke.

"Hello, Dr. Grant, how are you?" His words were carried along by a deep but gentle voice, and his question was followed by a warm and sincere smile. In those deep, soft eyes, though, there seemed to be a slight tinge of sadness.

There was something in his expression that caused my mind to immediately drop the previous moment's irritation at his interruption of my race to the next patient. Instead, I studied him carefully, tracing each wrinkled line on his face, hoping that one might lead me to the answer of who the man was and how he knew me.

He saw and correctly interpreted my mind's working.

"You don't remember me, do you?" he queried in his soft, rich voice. I made one last quick search of my memory. While it didn't provide the answer I sought, it did return a positive, warm feeling.

"I'm afraid I don't, sir. Have we met before?" As I continued to search his face for a clue, the radiance it had expressed moments before seemed to have dimmed slightly. But as he began to speak, it brightened once again.

"Yes, we have, Dr. Grant. You saved my wife's life." He spoke in an earnest tone, firmly squeezing my hand, his eyes reaching deep inside my mind, conveying a sincerity of appreciation that completely overwhelmed my soul.

His mannerisms, his words, and his facial expressions powerfully communicated to me his sense of heartfelt gratitude for some act or deed I had performed in the past that I still could not bring to mind. The strong emotion he imparted in such a simple yet meaningful manner humbled me.

Again, he read my searching mind.

"We came into this very emergency room about a year ago, and at that time, you diagnosed blood clots that were present in my wife's lungs. You started her on blood thinners and admitted her to the hospital."

Immediately, I knew the man and his wife but could not retrieve their names. "You and your wife are patients of Dr. Baker," I said. The man's smile brightened. "In fact, you were in this same room when I saw you before." My memory now began to rapidly serve up many of the details of their previous ER visit.

His wife had come in with a simple complaint—a cough—something we see in the ER just about every day. Yet hers was a little unusual. She had no runny nose, no scratchy throat, no fever, no aches, no wheezing, nor any of the other gazillion related symptoms that might cause one to hone in on a likely diagnosis.

Another thing my memory offered was that it was sudden in onset. No intermittent, slowly progressive onset of symptoms. She just suddenly had a cough out of the blue. It was most frequent and recurring at its onset but gradually diminished over the following hour or so.

The unusual way her cough began precipitated their decision to come to the ER, although after arriving, they began to wonder whether they should have come. Again, she had no other symptoms at that time, and they both felt they had overreacted.

I recalled that her heart rate had been in the upper nineties, even after she had been at rest on the stretcher for a while. It remained persistently elevated while she was in the ER.

Her physical exam was otherwise normal, with nothing to suggest the blood clots—no leg swelling or tenderness, no abnormal heart or lung sounds, no evidence or history of trauma, no pelvic infections or other processes that can be a risk factor for developing blood clots.

I remembered my discussion with them at that time. I told them I was concerned about the possibility of a blood clot in her legs or pelvis, or possibly even her heart, that had broken off and gone to her lungs. That could explain the sudden onset of her cough and also explain the continued elevation of her heart rate. However, all the tests we had run to that point in time didn't suggest that presumptive diagnosis.

I told them we could run a special type of test, a VQ scan, which could answer the question for us. Normally, we only do that test on patients with additional symptoms or findings, but I felt that it was indicated in her case, recognizing it might very well come back negative. That would make her workup for the onset of a cough an expensive evaluation.

After discussing it with them they had agreed to do the test. It came back positive. Mrs. Holden had thrown a blood clot to her lung. She was admitted to the hospital, where Dr. Baker came in to take care of her from that point forward.

Mr. Holden's eyes watered a little when he knew I actually did remember him and his wife. He then told me something I didn't know.

"Dr. Baker said that if you hadn't ordered that test, and instead just sent her home with a treatment for her cough, she would have most likely died. He said she probably would have thrown a bigger blood clot after the smaller one." He paused for a moment and then continued.

"Dr. Baker said that he would have missed it. He said he wouldn't have ordered the test." A tear rolled down the man's right cheek.

I could sense the intense love Mr. Holden had for his wife. In that brief moment, I could feel how much he cared for her and appreciated that she wasn't taken away from him that night they had previously come to the ER.

I was humbled by what Dr. Baker had told them. He was an incredibly competent and caring physician. That's why he was coming in to see Mrs. Holden in Room 16 this night. He could have had the ER doc see the patient, but instead, he would often come in to see his patients. That's how he preferred to practice medicine.

"Those were very kind words from Dr. Baker," I responded. "Knowing him, however, I imagine he would have had the same concerns I did and would have ordered the same test. He is a very humble man and an exceptional physician. We all think very highly of him."

I talked a little more with Mr. Holden and spoke with his wife, who was now being admitted to the hospital for a new problem. She had recently begun experiencing periodic, recurring numbness in her right leg.

Although I hated to leave their presence, other patients were waiting. I thanked Mr. Holden for speaking to me, and I told Mrs. Holden I would come by and check on her after I got off my shift in the morning.

As I moved from patient room to patient room that evening, I felt a sense of guilt for my initial negative thoughts when Mr. Holden first stepped into my path. I was expecting complaints and frustration, but instead, I received a depth of appreciation and warmth I have rarely experienced.

At around four thirty a.m., I finally caught up, having seen all patients in the ER with none waiting to be seen. Almost all had been discharged or admitted, which now gave me a chance to sit down and catch up on my documentation. As I did so, I intermittently reflected on what it would be like to have an office practice where I could schedule my patients rather than being overwhelmed with so many folks showing up at the same time.

I thought about what it would be like to develop longer-term relationships with my patients, like the Holdens, and see them over time, helping them with the various illnesses or injuries they might encounter.

As rewarding as that notion was, I also realized that type of medical practice would not fit my detail-oriented, somewhat perfectionist mindset. There would always be one more test to consider, one more reexamination, one more thing I could do for my patient. I knew I would probably never see my family. I would always be at the office or the hospital.

Time-boxing the window to provide patient care turned out to be a beneficial facet of the shift-based schedule in emergency medicine. Of course, the boundaries for those shifts often got pushed out a bit. Still, it allowed me the opportunity to have time for family and friends.

I thought about how ER physicians have such a short opportunity to bond with their patients. We often work in a compressed time frame that requires us to maximally utilize every second available to us and our patients.

As soon as the diagnosis and treatment have been provided, we must move on to the next patient. While patients may appreciate what we've done for them, we quickly become ghosts, disappearing from the longer time line of a patient's health care.

Rarely do we have the occasion to reflect upon the impact our care may have upon a patient and their family or friends. It is a satisfaction and comfort we often deny ourselves in our necessary rush to the next patient.

Mr. Holden was kind enough to interrupt that dash, offering me the precious gift of sincere gratitude for the impact I had upon his wife's life and his own, which were bound together through an extraordinary love for one another. I will always remember the warmth and depth of appreciation he expressed to me for the care I had provided his family.

He powerfully reminded me of why I went into medicine—so I could help my next patient.

~ ~ ~

Thank you for reading my book! I would love to hear your thoughts, and would be honored if you left a review or rating on Amazon— I read them all! You can scan the QR code below or log into your Amazon account and go to *The Next Patient* book page, customer reviews.

Thank you!
Dr. J. Thomas Grant

Medical Glossary

Angiocath: A short, thin, hollow piece of plastic tubing that is placed inside a patient's vein, through which medicines or IV fluids can be administered.

angiography: A diagnostic test in which a catheter is inserted into a blood vessel and advanced to a point where radiopaque dye is injected into the bloodstream. The dye will show up on X-rays, making the blood vessels and any blockages become visible.

arrested (in reference to a patient): A condition in which the heart has stopped functioning. There can be many different causes for this, with a heart attack being only one cause.

bag-valve-mask device (BVM): A medical device consisting of a handheld, self-inflating bag connected to a one-way valve and mask that covers the patient's nose and mouth. It is typically attached to a source of oxygen and is used by medical personnel to force air into the patient's lungs when the bag is squeezed.

BP: Acronym for "blood pressure."

cardiac monitor: An electronic device that continuously displays the electrical activity of the heart on a screen. Often times, the monitors are mounted above the bed. There are also portable cardiac monitors.

cardiopulmonary arrest: A term meaning the patient's heart has stopped functioning and the patient is not breathing.

cardiac tamponade: A very serious condition of the heart in which blood or fluid fills the saclike structure that surrounds the heart. As the sac fills with blood or fluid, it begins to take up space, compressing the heart, which progressively impedes the ability of the heart to fill its chambers and pump blood to the rest of the body. If it acutely develops, it can quickly lead to the death of the patient.

cervical collar: A type of neck brace that is often used in the prehospital/EMS setting to help limit the mobility of a patient's neck when concern exists for a possible spinal injury. They are typically made of a stiff plastic material with foam on the inside for comfort.

chest tube: A thick plastic tube, hollow on the inside and about the size of an adult's index finger. It is surgically inserted through the chest wall into the chest cavity, usually in an effort to expand a lung that has been collapsed by either blood or air that fills a portion of the chest cavity.

clinician: A person with medical knowledge or skills who cares for patients. That person could be a nurse, doctor, physician's assistant, nurse practitioner, paramedic, etc.

cardiopulmonary resuscitation (CPR): An attempt to restore a person's circulation and breathing after it has suddenly stopped. This typically involves the repeated compression of a person's chest, at times accompanied by some form of artificial breathing.

crash cart: A mobile cart with wheels that typically contains all of the drugs and equipment most commonly needed for patients requiring CPR. A cardiac monitor/defibrillator is usually on top of the cart.

crashed (in reference to a patient): Typically used to describe a patient who has suddenly decompensated. Often times, this is associated with a significant drop in blood pressure, loss of consciousness, respiratory arrest, seizure, or other substantial change in a patient's clinical status.

CT scan: A specialized type of X-ray that consists of many cross-sectional images of an area of the body that are combined by a computer to provide the physician with a very detailed and multidimensional view of the inside of the body.

CVP tray: A sterilized tray containing instruments necessary for the insertion of a large-bore needle through the skin and into a large blood vessel. A flexible plastic catheter is then inserted, after which the needle is retracted, leaving the catheter in place.

defibrillation: The procedure in which electrical energy is discharged through a patient's chest wall and heart muscle in an effort to "reset" the electrical pacemaker cells of the heart. The energy is delivered through two handheld paddles firmly pressed against the chest wall. Or, if the chest is open, two elongated paddles can be placed on each side of the visible heart.

defibrillator: The machine that generates and discharges electrical energy to a patient's heart when an ineffective heart rhythm exists, such as ventricular fibrillation. Varying degrees of energy can be selected depending upon the medical condition being treated as well as the specific heart rhythm that is being addressed.

DOA: Acronym for "dead on arrival."

electrocardiogram (EKG): A recording of the heart's electrical activity as viewed from multiple different vantage points on the patient's body. It is sometimes also called a "heart tracing." It is often printed out for review.

emergency department (ED)/emergency room (ER): These terms and their abbreviations are synonymous. In the very early years of medicine, the emergency room was often just that—a single room in the basement or at the back of the hospital where doctors might come to see their sick patients after office hours and determine whether they required hospitalization.

As medicine progressed, it became increasingly evident that the rapid and appropriate diagnosis and early treatment of a patient's serious illness or injury could significantly impact their subsequent survival.

Emergency rooms began to grow in size and importance in the urgent or emergent care of seriously ill or injured patients.

Emergency rooms evolved into larger and more organized emergency departments.

It soon became apparent that the better trained and more broadly knowledgeable physicians in the ER, the more likely they could provide the necessary treatment within the appropriate time frame. This led to the creation of the medical specialty of emergency medicine in the 1970s with residency programs subsequently established to provide the education and training for emergency care.

emergency medical services (EMS): A prehospital system established to provide emergency care and transportation to people outside the hospital. Oftentimes, such care is provided to those in accidents or those who have sudden, serious illnesses, such as heart attacks. The system also involves 911 dispatchers with prehospital instructions to assist those calling for help.

The EMS system may be a public entity (such as a fire department or "third service"), a volunteer organization, or a private entity usually contracted to provide service to a community. EMS systems typically operate under a physician medical director and may communicate with hospitals in real time for physician input or orders for specific medications or procedures.

EMTs: Acronym for emergency medical technicians. These individuals have received a specialized medical training course in the care of patients. The required knowledge and skills can vary by state. Paramedics are usually EMTs trained with additional knowledge, allowing them to administer a wider range of medications and perform more advanced skills such as intubation.

endotracheal tube: A flexible, hollow plastic tube that is inserted through the mouth and into the trachea (windpipe) to facilitate ventilation of a patient while also preventing fluids (such as vomitus) from entering the lungs. The tube has a circumferential balloon on its outside near the tip that goes inside the trachea. When the balloon is inflated, it helps to seal off the airway so blood or fluids cannot enter the lungs, thereby protecting them. The balloon cuff also helps to facilitate the movement of air and oxygen into and out of the lungs through the endotracheal tube.

etiology: A cause or basis for a disease.

extremis: A condition in which a patient is critically ill and near death.

GI: Abbreviation for "gastrointestinal."

GSW: Abbreviation for "gunshot wound."

gurney: A stretcher or ER "bed."

hematologic: A term meaning "related to the blood." Hematologic tests include a blood count, which is a measurement of the amount of blood a patient has in their body.

hematoma: A substantial collection of blood in the tissue.

history (in regard to medicine): The "story" the patient tells the clinician about their illness or injury. History taking is a critical skill for physicians.

hypoglycemia: Low blood sugar.

IM: Abbreviation for "intramuscular."

intubate/intubation: The process of inserting a plastic tube (endotracheal tube) into a person's airway.

intravenous (IV): This term often refers to an intravenous line that can be started on a patient for a variety of purposes, such as the administration of fluids or blood products, or access to the vascular system for the administration of drugs. An IV typically consists of the IV bag containing the fluids; the tubing that carries the fluids to the patient; and the Angiocath, which is inserted in the patient's vein and to which the IV tubing is connected.

joules: Used for measuring amounts of energy. When defibrillating a patient's heart, different amounts of energy can be used, as specified by the physician.

laryngoscope: An instrument used for looking inside a patient's throat, typically while they are lying flat on a stretcher and in a semiconscious or unconscious state. The instrument is L-shaped; the upper part of the L is called the handle, and the lower part of the L is referred to as the blade, although it is not sharp. There are different sizes and shapes of blades that can readily be changed out.

lumbar puncture (LP): Also referred to as a "spinal tap." A procedure performed by inserting a long needle containing a stylet through the skin of the lower back; between the bony processes on the back side of two adjacent vertebrae in the spine; and into the spinal canal, which contains a fluid-filled sac located within the bony canal.

Mayo stand: A small metal table that is movable. Typically, it stands about waist high with its top metal tray about twelve inches wide and eighteen inches long.

myocardial infarction (MI): A heart attack.

nasogastric (NG) tube: A soft, hollow, flexible tube of rubber or plastic that is typically passed through the nose, into and through the esophagus, and then into the stomach. It can be used to remove substances from the stomach, including air, or introduce substances into the stomach.

near drowning: A term used for nonfatal drowning in which the patient has not yet expired from the submersion.

nurse practitioner: An advanced-practice registered nurse with a degree of knowledge that allows them to diagnose and treat certain patients. Sometimes referred to as a mid-level practitioner.

OB: Abbreviation for "obstetrics."

OR: Acronym for "operating room."

oxygen saturation monitor: A device used to intermittently or continually measure the amount of oxygen in a patient's bloodstream. The device is often placed on the end of a patient's finger.

palpated: A medical term used to describe the action of a clinician as they examine a portion of the patient's body using touch.

patient history: Information obtained about a patient's illness or injury, often gathered through a clinician's questions (if the patient is conscious and capable of communicating). The patient history includes several components, such as the chief complaint, the history of the present illness, the past medical history, medications, allergies, social history, and the review of symptoms.

paramedics: Usually EMTs trained with additional knowledge, allowing them to administer a wider range of medications and perform more advanced skills such as intubation.

percussion: A method of tapping against different parts of the patient's body, typically using one's fingers, to gain information as part of a physical examination. The frequency and tone of the resulting sound can help to determine the presence of air or fluid in a given part of the body.

petechia: A small purplish or red dot on the skin that represents a very tiny amount of blood just under the outer layer of the skin. It is typically only one to two millimeters in size, and is not raised above the skin like a blister. Rather, it is just a colored dot. One or more petechiae can have minor or extremely serious implications depending upon the context of the illness and the reason behind their formation. The plural form is "petechiae."

physician's assistant: A clinician trained to diagnose and treat certain conditions and provide preventative care in partnership with a supervising physician. Sometimes referred to as a mid-level practitioner.

pneumothorax / pneumothoraces: The presence of air in the chest cavity between the outer lining of the lung and the chest wall, which can result in a collapsed lung. The plural form of pneumothorax is pneumothoraces (pneumothorax on both sides of the chest).

prep (of skin or wound): The process of cleansing the skin or wound with an antiseptic solution.

radial pulse: A pulse felt at the radial artery, found on the palm side of the wrist. If present, it usually means the patient's systolic blood pressure is at least ninety mm Hg. If absent, in an adult, it suggests the blood pressure is abnormally low.

resident: A physician who has graduated from medical school with a medical degree and entered a teaching program in which one cares for patients under the oversight or guidance of more experienced physicians. Typically, residents are referred to in relation to which year of training they are in, such as a second-year resident or third-year resident.

respiratory arrest: The patient stops breathing.

resuscitate: An effort to revive a patient who has expired or is critically ill and likely to soon expire.

resuscitation room: One or more specialized rooms in the ER where the necessary equipment and supplies are readily available for use in an effort to rapidly improve the status of a critically ill patient. Typically, it is a larger room where multiple clinicians can simultaneously access the patient. It is also designed to allow various pieces of testing equipment to be brought into the room. In some cases, such equipment may be mounted on the wall or ceiling.

scrubs/scrub suit: Simple clothing worn by physicians, nurses, and other health care providers who work in environments where their clothing is subject to potential stains or contamination. Scrubs are designed to be easily laundered and less expensive to replace if damaged or badly stained.

spinal tap: Another term for "lumbar puncture," or LP (see above).

stat: A common medical term meaning "immediate" or "right away." It comes from the Latin word "*statim.*"

stent placement: A stent is a small, tubelike structure that is inserted inside an artery and used to help keep it open. Typically, the stent is placed after a balloon angioplasty is performed to help open clogged arteries.

sterile field: A germ-free environment created through the use of antiseptics in combination with sterilized paper drapes free of any bacteria or viruses.

stylet: A probe or needle within a hollow tube or hollow needle. The needle used in a lumbar puncture has two parts—an inner needle or stylet that slides inside a hollow outer needle. The needle with the stylet in place is inserted through tissue, and once the tip of the needle is positioned inside the spinal canal, the inner needle or stylet is removed so spinal fluid can flow through the hollow outer needle and be collected.

suture: The "thread" used by clinicians to stitch together or sew up a wound. It comes in a variety of forms such as nylon, silk, absorbable, etc. Typically, the suture is attached to a curved needle used to puncture the skin through which the suture is then drawn. Using sutures to close a wound is often referred to as "getting stitches."

trachea: Medical term for "windpipe."

type and cross: A process of determining which blood type (A positive, A negative, B positive, B negative, AB positive, AB negative, O positive, O negative) can be given to a patient while minimizing the potential for a serious blood-transfusion reaction.

urinary catheter: A hollow, flexible tube made of rubber or similar material that is inserted through the urethra into the bladder to collect urine.

vasopressors: A type of medication administered through an IV line to raise or maintain a patient's blood pressure, keeping it from becoming too low.

ventricular fibrillation: A chaotic electrical rhythm that does not provide an orderly contraction of the heart muscle, thereby abolishing forward blood flow from the heart to the body. Unless quickly transformed to an effective heart rhythm, the patient will die.

About the Author

Dr. J. Thomas Grant is the pen name for a board-certified emergency medicine physician with more than twenty years of clinical experience, having worked in both academic and community hospital settings. He has seen tens of thousands of patients during his career, working with an array of dedicated providers in the emergency room and in prehospital EMS systems. Over the course of his professional practice he has served in a variety of roles and enjoyed participating in the education and training of physicians, nurses, paramedics, and EMTs.